Unit One
Resource Book

McDougal Littell

THE LANGUAGE OF
LITERATURE

GRADE NINE

McDougal Littell
A HOUGHTON MIFFLIN COMPANY
Evanston, Illinois • Boston • Dallas

ISBN 0-395-96795-3

10 11- CKI - 08 07 06 05

Unit One The Power of Storytelling

Part 2 Suspense and Surprise

To the Teacher

Each unit in *The Language of Literature* has its own resource book. This section provides an overview of all the resource materials found in the Unit Resource Books. Suggestions for using these materials to support and enhance the lessons in *The Language of Literature* are also provided. In using the Unit Resource Books for subsequent units, you may refer back to this overview for information about any of the components.

Description of Unit Resource Books

The copymasters in each book provide support for the contents of the Pupil's Edition and for instruction. The chart below lists the different types of copymasters in this book. A description of the pages and suggestions for their use follows the chart.

• Selection Summaries	
• Active Reading SkillBuilders	
• Literary Analysis SkillBuilders	Support the literary selections or group of selections in each unit
• Words to Know SkillBuilders	
• Selection Quizzes	
• Comparing Literature SkillBuilders	
• Grammar SkillBuilders	
• Building Vocabulary SkillBuilders	
• Writing Workshops	Support these special features in each unit
• Communication Workshops	
• Family and Community Involvement	Provide activities for reflecting on and extending the unit beyond the classroom
• Reflect and Assess	

Selection Summaries

These copymasters provide brief summaries of the literary selections in the Pupil's Edition. Real World Links, Literary Links, and Related Readings are not summarized, nor are lyric poems. Each summary includes descriptions of the characters and information about key events in the selection. By highlighting the essential elements of the selection that are necessary for comprehension, the summaries help students gain access to the selection. The summaries are also written at a level that allows students from any language background to use them comfortably.

Suggestions for Use:

The Selection Summaries can be used:
• to preview and review the selections
• to provide students with a meaningful context for each selection

- to assist students with limited English proficiency or comprehension difficulties in understanding the selections, especially those with intricate plots and complex language
- to serve as a review tool prior to taking selection tests.

Active Reading SkillBuilders

This one-page copymaster, provided for each selection, helps to increase reading comprehension by enabling students to interact with the text as they read. Each worksheet includes a brief review of the Active Reading skill in the Focus Your Reading section of the Pupil's Edition. It also supplies a graphic organizer that allows students to practice the skill as they read. This interaction helps students better understand the events, characters, main ideas, or form/genre of the selection.

Suggestions for Use:

The Active Reading worksheets should be distributed to all students before reading. Students may use the graphic organizer to interact with the text as they read.

Literary Analysis SkillBuilders

This one-page copymaster, provided for each selection, enables students to recognize and better understand the use of literary devices and styles. The worksheet includes a brief review of the Literary Analysis skill in the Pupil's Edition and supplies a graphic organizer that supports the skill. The worksheet may also include the cooperative learning or paired activity that appears in the Pupil's Edition after each selection.

Suggestions for Use:

The Literary Analysis worksheets should be distributed to students after they have finished reading each selection. Students may use the graphic organizer to identify examples of the literary devices and techniques.

Words to Know SkillBuilders

This one-page copymaster provides additional practice in using the vocabulary identified in the Words to Know section of the Pupil's Edition. Exercises include thematic paragraphs, poems, puzzles, and other activities that require students to use context clues to unlock word meaning. In addition, a writing activity is provided for students to retell or respond to the selection while incorporating the vocabulary words in their responses.

Suggestions for Use:

The Words to Know SkillBuilder worksheets should be distributed after students have completed the Words to Know vocabulary exercise in the Pupil's Edition. These SkillBuilder pages can also be used:

- to reteach the selected words from the selection
- to reinforce the meaning of the words from the selection so that students can integrate them into their working vocabularies

Selection Quizzes

This one-page copymaster provides a quick means of checking students' reading comprehension. Each quiz consists of five or ten questions, depending on the length of the selection. All quizzes appearing in this Unit Resource Book, as well as all questions printed in the Formal Assessment Book, can be found electronically on the Test Generator software.

Suggestions for Use:

The Selection Quiz worksheets should be distributed to students after they have completed the selection for a quick check of student's comprehension of key points in the selection. Selection Quiz pages can also be used:

- before reading to provide students with purpose-setting questions
- as a review of the selection in preparation for part and unit tests

Comparing Literature SkillBuilder

Whenever a graphic organizer is suggested in the Comparing Literature activities in the Pupil's Edition, this copymaster provides students a page on which to complete the activity.

Suggestions for Use

Comparing Literature SkillBuilder pages can be distributed for use by the students to help them complete the activities on the Comparing Literature pages of the Pupil's Edition.

Grammar SkillBuilders

This one-page copymaster provides additional exercises for the grammar concept taught on the Choices and Challenges page of the Pupil's Edition.

Suggestions for Use:

Grammar SkillBuilder pages can be given to students after they have read the selection. It can also be used:

- for additional instruction or practice
- as a review of the skill prior to testing

Building Vocabulary SkillBuilder

This one-page copymaster builds word-attack strategies using context clues and word-part analysis. Each page provides a brief reteaching of the vocabulary strategy taught on the Building Vocabulary page of the Pupil's Edition. It also includes additional practice exercises for the skill.

Suggestions for Use:

Building Vocabulary SkillBuilder pages can be used after students have completed the Building Vocabulary feature in the Pupil's Edition. It can also be used:

- as needed for additional instruction or practice
- as a review of word-attack strategies prior to testing

Writing Workshops

Each unit in the Pupil's Edition includes a Writing Workshop where students make connections between the unit literature, genre, or theme and their own lives and personal experiences.

Writing Workshop Support contains the following copymasters:

Prewriting—provides support, frequently in the form of a graphic organizer, to help students complete the prewriting activity introduced in the Pupil's Edition Writing Workshop feature.

Drafting and Elaboration—provides support for the drafting and elaboration instruction on the Pupil's Edition page. Each worksheet provides an unelaborated writing sample from the student essay presented in the Writing Workshop, data for students to draw on, and directions to help them revise the sample.

Peer Response Guide—provides a series of questions that students can use to elicit useful responses to their writing from their classmates. Students can ask for peer response at any stage of their writing process. The worksheet provides space for peer readers to offer responses and specific suggestions for revision.

Revising, Editing, and Proofreading—supplements the Drafting and Elaboration Guide Practice page. It provides questions to help students evaluate and revise their own writing. It also contains another rough excerpt from the student essay in the Writing Workshop with specific suggestions for revision.

Student Models—demonstrate strong, average, and weak responses to the same topic as that in the Pupil's Edition model. Each model is annotated to apply the rubrics for evaluating the writing in each sample.

Rubric for Evaluation—provided for assessing and evaluating student writing. Criteria for judging full, substantial, and little or partial accomplishment are presented.

Communication Workshop Support

The Pupil's Edition includes two Communication Workshops in which students use various forms of verbal and multimedia communication. The Communication Workshop copymasters provide support for the Pupil Edition activities, offer Standards for Evaluation, and, where appropriate, include a Student Model.

Family and Community Involvement

Family and Community Involvement copymasters are provided for each unit. Typically, these sheets provide options for a number of activities that students can complete with family members. Each of these activities is connected to the unit selections and themes. The instructions for these activities are directed to the family member, who then completes the activity with the student.

Reflect and Assess

Reflect and Assess copymasters offer students a convenient graphic organizer for completing one of the activities that appear in the Reflect and Assess feature in the Pupil's Edition.

Answer Key

The Answer Key provides specific or suggested answers, as appropriate, for these Unit Resource Book pages: Active Reading SkillBuilder, Literary Analysis SkillBuilder, Words to Know SkillBuilder, Selection Quiz, Building Vocabulary SkillBuilder, and Grammar SkillBuilder.

Unit One The Power of Storytelling

Family and Community Involvement

OPTION 1 Writing

Write an Autobiography

- **Purpose** To create autobiographies; to share memories of significant events while growing up
- **Connection** All of the selections in Unit One deal with a turning point in someone's life.
- **Materials** writing paper, a pen or pencil *or* a computer or a tape recorder and cassette tape
- **Activity** Most adults have memories of experiences and turning points that helped change or shape their lives as they approached adulthood. Talk with your teenager about your memories of growing up. Then ask your teenager to share memories of his or her own experiences. Work together to create a written or an oral autobiography of your teenager's life. You may wish to start by recording basic information on a form similar to the one shown.

Name: _____

Where and when I was born: _____

_____

My first home: _____

_____

When I first learned to walk/talk: _____

_____

My earliest memory: _____

_____

Events that shaped/changed my life:

1. _____

2. _____

3. _____

4. _____

Unit One The Power of Storytelling

Family and Community Involvement

OPTION 2 **Planning an Event**

Celebrate a Special Occasion

- **Purpose** To create a memorable experience to share together
- **Connection** Some of the selections in Unit One relate memorable experiences shared with others.
- **Materials** writing paper, a pen or pencil, a ruler (optional)
- **Activity** To create a shared memorable experience, plan an event with your teenager, such as a way to celebrate a special occasion, a holiday, or an activity that helps someone else. Your event may take the form of making a favorite recipe or learning a craft together, or volunteering time with a local charity or another community group. Afterward, talk with your teenager about the experience. If you wish, encourage him or her to record impressions on a chart like the one shown.

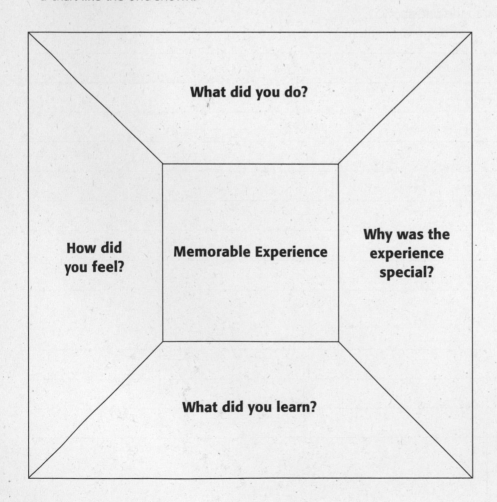

What did you do?

How did you feel?

Memorable Experience

Why was the experience special?

What did you learn?

Unit One The Power of Storytelling

Family and Community Involvement

OPTION 3 Viewing

Watch a Video

- **Purpose** To view and discuss a film depiction of young people growing up
- **Connection** Many of the selections in Unit One deal with painful experiences that become a part of growing up.
- **Materials** a TV and VCR, film that depicts young people reaching maturity, writing paper, a pen or pencil, a ruler
- **Activity** Many of the stories in Unit One depict how experiences, especially painful ones, can affect a young person's life. To promote a discussion on different maturing experiences, select a representative movie to watch together. Some examples include *Sixteen Candles, Rudy, How to Make an American Quilt,* and *A River Runs Through It.* These and other similar films are available at most video stores. After viewing the film, talk with your teenager about the main character's experiences, what he or she learned, and how his or her life changed as a result. If you wish, encourage your teenager to record impressions on a chart like the one shown.

Film Title: _____

Character's Name: _____

What He or She Experienced	What He or She Learned	How His or Her Life Changed as a Result

The Necklace

Guy de Maupassant

Summary

Setting: Paris, second half of the 19th century

Madame Loisel is unhappy. She wants to live the life of the rich. She and her husband have little money. They are invited to a fancy party. They cannot go unless Madame Loisel has a dress to wear, so they use their savings to buy a dress. Then she borrows a diamond necklace from a rich friend. Madame Loisel has a wonderful time at the party. Everyone admires her. On the way home, she loses the necklace. She is too embarrassed to tell her friend what has happened. Madame Loisel and her husband borrow a lot of money to buy a necklace just like the one she lost. She takes the new necklace to her friend. For ten years, the Loisels work long and weary hours to repay the money they borrowed. Madame Loisel now looks old and rough. One day she meets her friend. She tells her the whole story. Her friend says that the original necklace was not made of real diamonds. It was worth very little money.

The Necklace (page 26)

📖 Active Reading SkillBuilder

Cause and Effect

Events in a plot are sometimes linked causally. One event causes another, which causes another, and so on until the end of the story. A series of events linked in this way is called a chain of **cause and effect.** Use the diagram to connect the major events of "The Necklace" in an unbroken chain of cause and effect. Add links to the diagram if necessary.

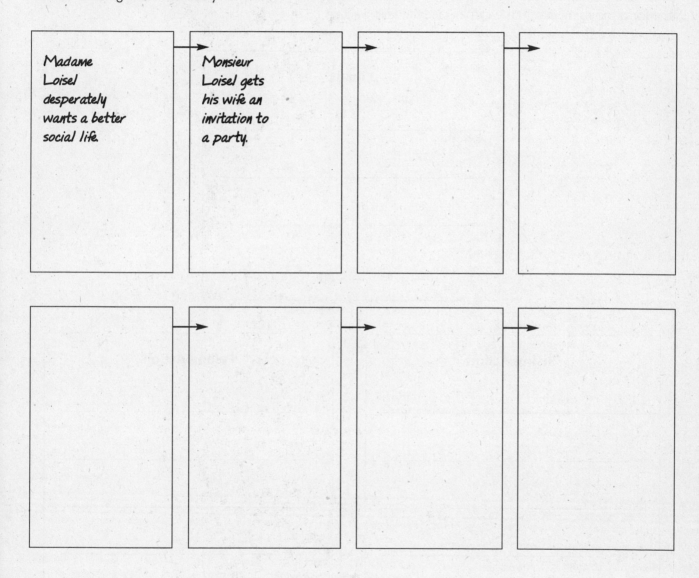

| Madame Loisel desperately wants a better social life. | Monsieur Loisel gets his wife an invitation to a party. | | |

The Necklace (page 26)
Literary Analysis SkillBuilder

Plot

The events that make up the **plot** of a story can be divided into rising action and falling action. The rising action consists of the conflicts and complications faced by the main character. Rising action leads to the climax, or turning point, of the story. The falling action, or resolution, occurs at the end of the story and shows how the conflicts are resolved. Use the diagram below to outline events in "The Necklace" that form the rising action, the climax, and the falling action.

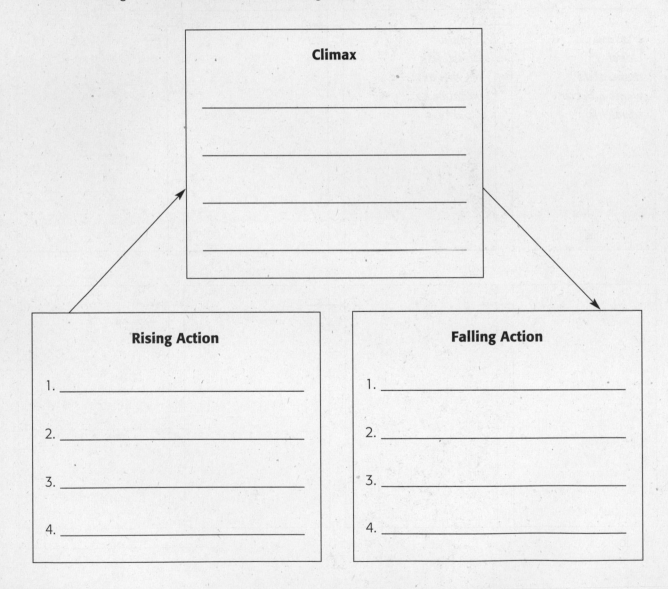

Climax

_____

_____

_____

_____

Rising Action

1. _____

2. _____

3. _____

4. _____

Falling Action

1. _____

2. _____

3. _____

4. _____

Follow Up: Which events that form the rising action of "The Necklace" are conflicts, or struggles between opposing forces? Which are complications that cause difficulties for the characters? Write *conflict* or *complication* next to each event.

The Necklace (page 26)

Words to Know SkillBuilder

Words to Know

adulation	askew	gamut	privation	ruinous
aghast	exorbitant	pauper	prospects	vexation

A. Decide which word from the word list belongs in each numbered blank.
Then write the word on the blank line on the right.

You tell him, every day, he's perfect. I have one objection.
With every word you say, he wanders further from perfection.   (1)
He's turning out conceited, and he's losing every friend.
I wish your (1) of your darling boy would end.

_____ (2)

If I don't learn that I must be a less devoted shopper,
I'll go so far in debt that I will end up as a (2).

_____ (3)

She read a comic during class. She slept throughout the test.
Although she hopes that she will pass, her (3) aren't the best.

_____ (4)

I'm sure the pie is very nice,
But 15 dollars for a slice
Is too (4) a price.

_____ (5)

The desert that I had to cross was burning hot and vast.
I stood and stared, astonished, feeling helpless and (5).

_____ (6)

I didn't have insurance when the wind blew down the tree,
Which landed on my house and proved quite (6) to me.

_____ (7)

I spent my winter gladly in a state of true (7),
So that I'd have the money for a summertime vacation.

_____ (8)

You promise you will be on time, so that's my expectation;
And when you're late, I must admit to feeling some (8).

_____ (9)

I know your clothes are all brand new,
But I'd be more impressed with you
If your silk necktie weren't (9).

_____ (10)

I looked upon the (10) of the shades of blue, and I
Found many represented in the colors of the sky.

B. Imagine that you are an advice columnist and that *either* M. or Mme. Loisel has
written to you at some point (any point) in the story. Reply, using at least **five** of the
Words to Know.

The Necklace (page 37)

Grammar Skillbuilder: Abstract and Concrete Nouns

Key Concept: Writers select abstract nouns to emphasize ideas and feelings, and concrete nouns to emphasize qualities that can be perceived.

Abstract Nouns

An **abstract noun** names ideas, qualities, or feelings that cannot be perceived through the senses. Maupassant uses abstract nouns to describe the feelings of the main character, Madame Loisel.

"And she would weep for days on end from **vexation, regret, despair,** and **anguish.**"

Concrete Nouns

A **concrete noun** names an object that can be seen, heard, smelled, touched, or tasted. Here Maupassant uses concrete nouns to define the materialistic world of which Madame Loisel dreams.

"She would dream of great reception **halls** hung with old **silks,** of fine **furniture** filled with priceless **curios,** . . ."

Activity

Rewrite each sentence using abstract nouns if the original sentence contains concrete nouns, or concrete nouns if the original sentence contains abstract nouns. Begin your new sentence with the sentence starter in parentheses. Underline the nouns in your new sentences.

1. Mathilde Loisel had no status, no prospects that would permit her to marry a man of rank. (Mathilde Loisel lacked . . .)

2. Though she was attractive and charming, she finally married a minor clerk. (Though she had . . .)

3. The walls of her apartment seem dingy to her, the chairs threadbare, the draperies faded. (Her apartment looks . . .)

4. The invitation to an evening reception brings tears to her eyes. (Her reaction to the invitation is . . .)

5. She insists that she has nothing appropriate to wear. (She says she has no suitable . . .)

6. Her husband gives her money for an evening dress. (Her husband responds with . . .)

7. She looks at the adornments in her friend's collection, considering what to borrow. (She examines the . . .)

8. She is wildly happy and successful the evening of the reception. (She dances . . .)

9. When she loses the necklace, she collapses helplessly in a chair. (She reacts to the loss with . . .)

10. Mme. Loisel must make many sacrifices to repay the loans. (Mme. Loisel learns to . . .)

The Necklace (page 26)

Selection Quiz

Recall the events in the story. Then answer the questions in phrases or sentences.

1. Why doesn't Madame Loisel enjoy her life at the beginning of the story?

_____

_____

_____

2. How does Madame Loisel go about getting something special to wear to the party?

_____

_____

_____

3. What happens after the Loisels arrive home from the party?

_____

_____

_____

4. Why doesn't Madame Loisel tell her friend right away about her loss?

_____

_____

_____

5. What surprises Madame Loisel when she finally tells her friend the truth?

_____

_____

_____

The Most Dangerous Game

Richard Connell

Summary

Setting: A tropical island in the Caribbean, 20th century

Sanger Rainsford is a famous hunter. It is night. He is sailing past the mysterious Ship-Trap Island. He hears gun shots. He loses his balance and falls overboard. Then he swims to the island. The next day he meets General Zaroff. Zaroff is also a hunter. He explains to Rainsford that he has become bored with hunting tigers and other dangerous animals. Now he hunts humans. He invites Rainsford to join him. Rainsford refuses. So Zaroff decides to hunt Rainsford. Zaroff tells Rainsford that if Rainsford can stay alive for three days, he can leave the island. In the woods, Rainsford uses his hunting skills to stay alive. Finally he jumps from a cliff into the sea to save himself from Zaroff and his dogs. Zaroff thinks the hunt is over. But Rainsford surprises Zaroff and kills him. He has outwitted Zaroff at his own deadly game.

The Most Dangerous Game (page 38)

📖 Active Reading SkillBuilder

Predicting

A **prediction** is an attempt to answer the question, "What will happen next?" To make predictions, notice the following in a story:

- interesting details about character, plot, and setting
- unusual statements made by the main characters
- foreshadowing—hints about future plot twists

As you read "The Most Dangerous Game," record three predictions, as well as your reasons for each guess.

Prediction	Reasons
1.	
2.	
3.	

The Most Dangerous Game (page 38)

Literary Analysis SkillBuilder

Conflict

Most stories are built around a central **conflict,** or struggle between people, or between people and nature, an obstacle, or society. Sometimes the struggle may go on inside a character. An **external conflict** involves a character pitted against an outside force. An **internal conflict** occurs when the struggle takes place within a character's own mind. List instances of each kind of conflict in the story. Then answer the questions.

Internal Conflict
Zarnoff
Rainsford

External Conflict
Person vs. Person
Person vs. Nature
Person vs. Obstacle

Follow Up: Which conflicts added the most excitement to the story? Which revealed something important about one of the characters? Explain. Why do you think Connell included the other conflicts that you identified?

The Most Dangerous Game (page 38)

Words to Know SkillBuilder

Words to Know

affable	deplorable	elude	scruple	tangible
amenity	disarming	imperative	solicitously	uncanny
condone	droll	quarry	stamina	zealous

A. On each blank line, write the word from the word list that the clue describes.

1. This is a word politicians always seem to use to describe the living conditions in slums.

   _____

2. This is a word you would hope people you want to make friends with would use to describe you.

   _____

3. This describes the air of confidence that calms your worries about a surgeon's skill.

   _____

4. This is something that isn't a necessity but is nice to have (like a salt shaker or a telephone).

   _____

5. This might be the word you'd choose to describe a person who seemed able to read your mind.

   _____

6. This describes a book but not the ideas in it, a flower but not its smell, a valentine but not the feeling it gives you.

   _____

7. This is how one says, "Are you sure you're all right? Can I do anything to help?"

   _____

8. This describes those things you really must have and those things you really must do.

   _____

B. For each phrase in the first column, find the phrase in the second column that is closest in meaning. Write the letter of that phrase in the blank.

_____	1. regretful prey	A. elude the rude
_____	2. zealous protection	B. condone cologne
_____	3. a droll rabbit	C. a sorry quarry
_____	4. permit perfume	D. pupils' scruples
_____	5. students' morals	E. a funny bunny
_____	6. a fish's endurance	F. intense defense
_____	7. avoid the unmannerly	G. a salmon's stamina

C. Write a character sketch of General Zaroff using at least **five** of the Words to Know.

The Most Dangerous Game (page 60)

Grammar SkillBuilder: Choosing Precise Verbs

Key Concept: Experienced writers often avoid using such common verbs as *be*, *have*, *make*, *go*, *say*, and *lie*. Instead they use more precise verbs to clarify meaning, create vivid images, and strengthen the mood of their writing.

Precise Verbs

Verbs are the most powerful words in sentences. They convey action, movement, and sometimes the drama of thoughts and observations. When revising your writing, try to make your ideas as clear as possible. For example, in the following sentences the verb *wanders* is more precise and conveys a more vivid image than the verb *walks*.

Common Verb: He **walks** along the narrow deck.

Precise Verb: He **wanders** along the narrow deck.

Activity

Replace each underlined verb in these sentences with a verb that creates a more vivid picture. Make sure that the verbs you select agree in number with their subjects.

1. Rainsford <u>is</u> in a steamer chair on deck in the quiet Carribbean night, when suddenly the distant sound of gunfire startles him.

2. Rainsford <u>stands</u> up and moves quickly to the railing.

3. He <u>gets</u> up on the railing.

4. Losing his balance, he <u>falls</u> into the warm sea waters.

5. After swimming strenuously to shore, he <u>pulls</u> himself out of the water.

6. Two nights of fear <u>go</u> by at a snail's pace.

7. He <u>lies</u> out on a tree limb so he can watch through a screen of leaves.

8. Rainsford <u>stops</u> there with every muscle ready to spring.

9. Like popping a balloon, the air <u>comes</u> from Rainsford's lungs.

10. He knows it is useless to <u>walk</u> through the dense jungle at night.

The Most Dangerous Game (page 38)
Selection Quiz

Recall the events and characters in the story. Then answer the questions in phrases or sentences.

1. What is Rainsford's attitude toward hunting at the beginning of the story?

_____

_____

_____

2. How does Rainsford meet General Zaroff on the island?

_____

_____

_____

3. What does General Zaroff propose to Rainsford?

_____

_____

_____

4. How do Rainsford's past experiences as a hunter help him on the island?

_____

_____

_____

5. Why is Zaroff surprised to see Rainsford at the end of the story?

_____

_____

_____

Where Have You Gone, Charming Billy?

Tim O'Brien

Summary

Setting: Vietnam, late 1960s

It is Paul Berlin's first night in the Vietnam War. He is a soldier. He and his platoon are walking through enemy territory. They are going to a safe beach. Berlin is afraid. He tries to pretend that he is on a camping trip with his father. But he keeps thinking about Billy Boy Watkins. Earlier in the day, a land mine had exploded and Billy Boy had lost his foot. Billy Boy had been so afraid of dying that he had had a heart attack and died. The event has made Berlin very afraid. He tries to trick himself into not thinking about it.

   The platoon stops to rest. Berlin and another soldier talk about Billy Boy's death. Berlin begins giggling nervously. He cannot stop. The other soldier smothers Paul until he is finally quiet. The platoon moves on toward the beach. Berlin is shaking. He is still afraid.

Where Have You Gone, Charming Billy? (page 62)

📖 Active Reading SkillBuilder

Making Inferences

When readers make a logical guess about something in a story, based on information in the story and their own common sense, they are making an **inference.** Use the chart below to record clues that help you understand who Paul Berlin is and what he is going through. Pay special attention to what he does with his body, what he notices in his surroundings, and what he thinks about.

Private First Class Paul Berlin		
Statement in Story	**Common Sense**	**Inference**
"He pretended he was not a soldier."	People pretend that things they wish were true <u>are</u> true.	Paul does not like being a soldier.

Where Have You Gone, Charming Billy? (page 62)

Literary Analysis SkillBuilder

Character

Most short stories center on the experiences and actions of one or more **main characters**. Their experiences, reactions, and changes are the focus of the story. **Minor characters** interact with the main characters and help move the story along. Use the spider map to illustrate how the minor characters in this story affect the main character, Paul Berlin.

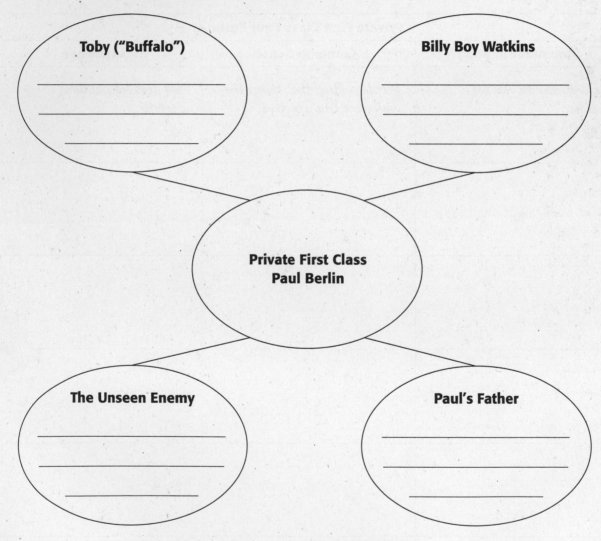

Follow Up: On the lines below, identify Paul's conflict and whether it is primarily external or internal. Then, with a group of classmates, discuss which minor characters contribute to Paul's conflict and which help him resolve it.

_____

_____

Where Have You Gone, Charming Billy? (page 62)

Words to Know SkillBuilder

Words to Know

casually	consolation	elegantly	inertia	silhouetted
conical	diffuse	execute	primitive	transparent

A. Circle the word in each group that is closest in meaning to the boldfaced word.

1. **consolation**	grief	hope	gratitude	comfort
2. **elegantly**	gracefully	quickly	happily	efficiently
3. **execute**	prevent	perform	eliminate	consider
4. **diffuse**	confusing	definite	unfocused	different
5. **silhouetted**	brilliant	outlined	visible	prominent
6. **casually**	informally	thoughtfully	immediately	carefully
7. **transparent**	opaque	presentable	clear	murky

B. Fill in the blank in each sentence with the correct Word to Know.

1. Only a corner of the muddy windshield was _____ enough to see through.

2. He noticed a weird shape _____ against the stormy sky.

3. The image was _____, like a photograph out of focus.

4. Top to bottom, the shape was _____, similar to that of a tornado.

5. The scene looked strange and _____, like something from prehistoric times.

6. In his truck, he sat and stared, as if _____ kept him from moving.

7. Finally, the shape passed gracefully and _____ beyond the distant hills.

8. He decided that only a film crew could _____ so mysterious a vision.

C. Write a letter to Tim O'Brien, the author of "Where Have You Gone, Charming Billy?" Tell him your reactions to his story. Include at least **three** Words to Know in your letter.

Where Have You Gone, Charming Billy? (page 73)

Grammar SkillBuilder: Adverbs

Key Concept: Writers use adverbs for clarity—to help their readers more clearly visualize or understand an action, a character, or a scene.

Adverbs

An **adverb** modifies a verb, an adjective, or another adverb. Adverbs supply additional information about *when, where, how much,* or *to what extent* something happens or is done. Look at the following examples of adverbs from Tim O'Brien's short story "Where Have You Gone, Charming Billy?"

Modifying a Verb: "So he walked **carefully,** counting his steps."

Modifying an Adjective: "The soldier's hand was **strangely** warm and soft."

Modifying an Adverb: ". . . now the fear was mostly the fear of being **so** terribly afraid again."

Activity

For each sentence, supply an adverb to modify the underlined word or words. Identify the modified word as a verb, an adjective, or an adverb.

1. Although the soldiers were given special training, many of them were <u>anxious</u>.

2. Some people <u>appear</u> calm, no matter what the difficulty.

3. When darkness fell, the platoon <u>moved</u> in single file without speaking a word.

4. He <u>crawled</u> toward his rifle.

5. He looked away so he would not be <u>afraid</u>.

6. The rifle felt <u>heavy</u> in his grasp.

7. They <u>marched</u> from the village, moving <u>silently</u>.

8. As he <u>followed</u> the others in his platoon, he <u>tried</u> to remember what he had been taught.

9. They <u>waited</u> in the tall grass for clouds to cover the brightness of the moon.

10. He hoped that when they <u>reached</u> the sea he would do <u>better</u>.

Where Have You Gone, Charming Billy? (page 62)

Selection Quiz

Recall the events in the story. Then answer the questions in phrases or sentences.

1. Where is Private Paul Berlin and why?

_____

_____

_____

2. What are some reasons for his fear?

_____

_____

_____

3. Berlin tries several strategies to deal with his fear. Name two and tell how well they work for him.

_____

_____

_____

4. What does Billy Boy Watkins have to do with Berlin and his experience?

_____

_____

_____

5. Why is it important that Toby stop Berlin's giggling?

_____

_____

_____

Marigolds

Eugenia Collier

Summary

Setting: Rural shantytown, early 1930s

Lizabeth recalls something that happened when she was 14. It is during the Great Depression. Many people have lost their jobs. New jobs are hard to find. Her family lives in a rural African-American area. Her mother works for a white family. Her father leaves home every day to look for a job. Lizabeth, her brother Joey, and other neighborhood children look after themselves. For fun, they like to bother Miss Lottie. Miss Lottie is an old woman who grows marigolds. Her flower garden is the only pretty thing in the poor and dusty neighborhood. One day, Lizabeth leads the children in throwing rocks at the marigolds. She yells at Miss Lottie. Later, Lizabeth feels ashamed. That night she wakes up. She hears her parents talking about their money problems. Her father cries. Lizabeth is upset. She gets up early. She and Joey go back to Miss Lottie's garden. She wildly pulls up the marigolds. Then she sees Miss Lottie standing in front of her. Lizabeth sees that Miss Lottie is sad. Lizabeth knows that she is not a child any more. Looking back on this day, Lizabeth sees it as the beginning of being an adult.

Marigolds (page 74)

📖 Active Reading SkillBuilder

Drawing Conclusions

Understanding literature requires readers to **draw conclusions** about events, causes of events, characters, and so on. In drawing conclusions, readers combine information from the text with their own prior knowledge. Note places in "Marigolds" where you find yourself drawing a conclusion that helps you understand the story. Use the chart to record your conclusions.

Drawing Conclusions About "Marigolds"		
Text Information	**Prior Knowledge**	**Conclusion**
All the narrator remembers of her hometown is the dust.	People remember pleasant experiences.	The narrator didn't have many pleasant experiences in her hometown.

Marigolds (page 74)

Literary Analysis SkillBuilder

Setting

The time and place of the action of a story is called the **setting.** The setting often plays an important role in the plot and makes a strong contribution to the story's overall impact and meaning. In some stories, the setting is simple and straightforward. In others, it can be more complex, taking place in a character's private world of memory or feelings. Locate two passages from "Marigolds" in which the description of the setting seems to express the narrator's feelings.

	Feelings the Setting Expresses
Passage 1	
Passage 2	

Follow Up: Underline vivid descriptive phrases in the passages on your chart. Then use these phrases to create a poem. Share your poem with the class.

Marigolds (page 74)

Words to Know SkillBuilder

Words to Know

bravado	degradation	impotent	perverse	squalor
compassion	futile	impoverished	poignantly	stoicism

A. Fill in each set of blanks with the correct word from the word list. Then use the boxed letters to complete the sentence below the puzzle.

1. This is shown by a tiny dog who barks madly at a huge dog only when it's on the other side of the fence.   _ _ _ _ _ ☐ _

2. People may say, "My hands are tied" when they feel that this describes them.   _ _ _ _ _ ☐ _ _

3. This describes someone one who is broke, down and out, and can't make ends meet.   _ _ ☐ _ _ _ _ _ _ _ _

4. This is what's going on if you come down in the world or fall into disgrace.   _ _ _ ☐ _ _ _ _ _ _

5. People might say this describes someone who argues for the sake of arguing.   _ _ _ _ _ ☐ _

6. When you want to do something about a sad state of affairs, this is what you are feeling.   _ _ _ _ _ _ ☐ _ _

7. This is a quality crybabies do *not* have and that people who lie quietly on a bed of nails do have.   _ _ _ _ _ _ _ ☐ _ _

8. This describes crying over spilled milk, going on a wild goose chase, or trying to empty the sea with a cup.   _ _ _ ☐ _

9. If your parent says this is the condition your room is in, I hope it's an exaggeration!   _ _ _ _ _ ☐ _ _

10. If a movie presents events this way, it may be described as a "two-hankie movie" or a "tear-jerker."   _ _ _ _ _ _ ☐ _ _ _ _

Complete the following sentence with the word that the boxed letters spell out.

"Marigolds" takes place during the _____.

B. What might Lizabeth have said to Miss Lottie to try to explain her behavior? Write a short apology that uses at least **five** of the Words to Know.

Marigolds (page 74)

Grammar SkillBuilder: Compound Adjectives

Key Concept: Writers often use compound adjectives to make their characters and settings come alive. For variety, writers sometimes place the adjectives after, rather than before, the word they modify.

Compound Adjectives

Two or more adjectives that modify the same noun or pronoun are called **compound adjectives.** Compound adjectives may be two or more words (*little barefoot boy; fast* and *furious* race), or hyphenated words (*wind-borne* dust; *well-written* story). When placed after the noun or pronoun, compound adjectives are not hyphenated (The story was *well written*).

Before the Noun: Miss Lottie's bent frame still showed traces of a **tall, powerful** woman.

Before and After the Noun: Her home was a **falling-down** shack, **sagging and rotting.**

As Predicate Adjective: Her flowers were **golden** and **dazzling.**

Remember to use a comma between two or more adjectives of equal rank that modify the same word. Adjectives are of equal rank if placing *and* between them sounds natural and if you can reverse their order without changing the meaning.

Activity

Insert compound adjectives to modify the underlined nouns and pronouns in these sentences.

1. The narrator recalls the <u>summer</u> that marked the end of her innocence.

2. The <u>children</u> gather in the dusty yard.

3. Impulsively, they torment Miss Lottie, who is working in her garden of <u>marigolds</u>.

4. <u>Miss Lottie</u> is old.

5. She reacts furiously to the <u>attack</u> on her flowers.

6. Lizabeth discovers that her <u>father</u> is bitterly unhappy about being unable to provide for his family.

7. Lizabeth's <u>mood</u> drives her to destroy the marigolds.

8. Immediately <u>she</u> is sorry.

9. She comes to regard her <u>act</u> as marking the end of her childhood.

10. Years later she plants marigolds in memory of that <u>time</u>.

Marigolds (page 74)

Selection Quiz

Recall the events in the story. Then answer the questions in phrases or sentences.

1. When Lizabeth thinks about her hometown, what does she remember about it?

   _____

   _____

   _____

2. When she looks back on herself at age 14, what does she remember?

   _____

   _____

   _____

3. What are two things Lizabeth remembers about Miss Lottie, her house,
   or her yard?

   _____

   _____

   _____

4. How do Lizabeth, her brother, and her friends annoy Miss Lottie?

   _____

   _____

   _____

5. What does Lizabeth do after she overhears her mother and father talking in the
   middle of the night?

   _____

   _____

   _____

Two Kinds

Amy Tan

Summary

Setting: Chinatown, San Francisco, 1960s

In China, Jing-mei's mother lost her mother, father, home, first husband, and twin baby daughters. Now she is remarried and lives in the United States. She hopes that Jing-mei will be a big success. She has Jing-mei's hair cut to look like Shirley Temple's. She tries to make Jing-mei memorize state capitals. Then she sees a Chinese girl playing the piano on television. She decides that Jing-mei will be a great pianist. She arranges for Jing-mei to take lessons from their neighbor, Mr. Chong. Mr. Chong is a retired piano teacher. He is now deaf. Jing-mei figures out that Mr. Chong cannot hear her play. She does not try at all and learns very little. Then she plays poorly at a talent show. This performance embarrasses Jing-mei and her family, especially her mother. Her mother, though, does not say anything about the bad performance. She expects Jing-mei to continue playing the piano. Jing-mei refuses. Jing-mei and her mother have a big argument. Jing-mei shouts that her mother wants Jing-mei to be something she's not. Her mother never asks her to play the piano again. Years later, her mother gives Jing-mei the piano for her 30th birthday. After her mother dies, Jing-mei plays it.

Two Kinds (page 88)

📖 Active Reading SkillBuilder

Making Judgments

In "Two Kinds," the mother and daughter each have a number of complaints about the other. To **make a judgment** about which of the complaints is justified, decide what criteria or standards to apply to the situation. In the box below, list the most important criteria. Using the chart below, write two complaints made by each character. Note whether they are justified according to your criteria.

```
┌──────────────────────────────────────────────────────────────┐
│                        List of Criteria                        │
│   _____  │
│   _____  │
│   _____  │
│   _____  │
└──────────────────────────────────────────────────────────────┘
```

Mother's Complaints	Daughter's Complaints
1. _____ _____ Justified?_____ _____ _____	1. _____ _____ Justified?_____ _____ _____
2. _____ _____ Justified?_____ _____ _____	2. _____ _____ Justified?_____ _____ _____

Two Kinds (page 88)

Literary Analysis SkillBuilder

Theme

Theme is the main idea, or message, in a work of fiction. It is a perception about life or human nature that a writer shares with the reader. The theme can sometimes be inferred from the characters and what they learn in a story. Record on the chart what the mother and daughter each learn from the mother's high expectations in "Two Kinds." Use this information to consider what the author wants to convey to the reader. Then compose a sentence or two to state the story's theme.

What Daughter Learns	What Mother Learns

Theme

_____

_____

_____

Two Kinds (page 88)

Words to Know SkillBuilder

Words to Know

betrayal	discordant	indignity	prodigy	reproach
devastate	fiasco	lament	ream	reverie

A. Decide which word from the word list belongs in each numbered blank.
Then write the word on the blank line on the right.

A very young lady from Glasgow
Gave a concert that was a (1).
That girl's vocal coach
Surely merits (2),
For she sang like she'd swallowed Tabasco.

(1) _____

Now, a (3) is a great treasure,
A child with skill beyond measure.
And the sounds from this youth
Left us gasping, in truth,
But from agony rather than pleasure.

(2) _____

I'd thought only a tormented cat
Could (4) music like that.
She ruined each note
Coming forth from her throat,
And the few that survived were all flat.

(3) _____

It's hard to believe there could be
As (5) a singer as she.
First one note, then another,
At war with each other,
As if they would never agree.

(4) _____

(5) _____

B. For each phrase in the first column, find the phrase in the second column that is
closest in meaning. Write the letter of that phrase in the blank.

_____ 1. each fantasy

_____ 2. appears to be a lot

_____ 3. while expecting an indignity

_____ 4. agree to mourn

_____ 5. a betrayal of the monarchs

A. seems to be reams

B. consent to lament

C. a disloyalty to royalty

D. every reverie

E. in anticipation of humiliation

C. In "Two Kinds," the narrator's idea of what will happen at the performance differs
from what actually occurs. Contrast her expectations with the reality of the situation,
using at least **five** of the Words to Know.

Name _____   Date _____

Two Kinds (page 102)

Grammar SkillBuilder: Verb Phrases

Key Concept: Writers sometimes use the repetition of verb phrases to emphasize a particular trait or quality, to convey information about a character or scene, or to compare the characteristics of characters.

Verb Phrases

A **verb phrase** consists of a main verb—either action or linking—and one or more helping verbs. In a sentence with a verb phrase, it is the first helping verb that must agree with its subject in number. For example, in the following sentence the verb phrase *has been translated* contains the helping verbs *has* and *been.* The helping verb *has* is singular in number to agree with the subject *book,* which is also singular.

Example: Amy Tan's book, *The Joy Luck Club,* **has been translated** into more than 15 languages.

Activity

Rewrite each sentence, replacing the verb in parentheses with a verb phrase. Choose from these helping verbs: *am, is, are, was, were, be, being, been, have, has, had, do, does, did, shall, will, can, may, could, should, would, might, must.*

1. Amy Tan (write) the book titled *The Joy Luck Club.*

2. In 1989 the book (list) for eight months as a *New York Times* bestseller.

3. Yes, the book (make) into a movie.

4. In *The Joy Luck Club,* stories about four Chinese women and their American-born daughters (weave) together.

5. One such story is "Two Kinds," which (narrate) by a young woman who is the daughter of Chinese immigrants.

6. The young woman's mother believed that in America you (be) anything you wanted to be.

7. To discover her daughter's special talent, the mother (give) her daughter tests based on stories about child prodigies.

8. During the talent show, the daughter (focus) more on how lovely she looked than on how well she played the piano.

9. The daughter (become) a good pianist, but she refused to try.

10. When the daughter was an adult, her mother still contended that she (is) a genius if she had wanted to.

Two Kinds (page 88)

Selection Quiz

Recall the events in the story. Then answer the questions in phrases or sentences.

1. How does Jing-mei react at first to her mother's plans to make her a prodigy?

   _____

   _____

   _____

2. Why does Jing-mei change her mind about becoming a prodigy?

   _____

   _____

   _____

3. What does Jing-mei learn from Mr. Chong?

   _____

   _____

   _____

4. What happens to Jing-mei at the talent show?

   _____

   _____

   _____

5. What happens between Jing-mei and her mother when her mother insists that
   she practice, despite what happened at the talent show?

   _____

   _____

   _____

Name _____   Date _____

Understanding Context Clues (page 103)
Building Vocabulary SkillBuilder

Some Types of Context Clues	
Definition and Restatement Clue	a restatement of the word's definition
Example Clue	uses examples to demonstrate the word's meaning
Comparison Clue	compares the word to a similar word or idea
Contrast Clue	contrasts the word with another word or idea

Use context clues to define each underlined word. Then identify the kind of context
clue that led you to each definition.

1. They had quite an <u>altercation</u> last night, and we could hear them yelling from down the street.

   Definition: _____ **Type of context clue:** _____

2. He tried to <u>cajole</u> his friend to drive him to the party, but his friend saw right through his schemes.

   Definition: _____ **Type of context clue:** _____

3. That dog is as <u>cantankerous</u> as a stubborn mule.

   Definition: _____ **Type of context clue:** _____

4. Did she <u>concur</u> with the judges' decision, or was she displeased with the outcome?

   Definition: _____ **Type of context clue:** _____

5. By not commenting on her poor behavior, we are <u>condoning</u> it.

   Definition: _____ **Type of context clue:** _____

6. Alexandria is <u>oblivious</u> to the robbery—it is as if she wasn't even in the restaurant at the time.

   Definition: _____ **Type of context clue:** _____

7. I will <u>defer</u> to your judgment because you know more about the situation than I do.

   Definition: _____ **Type of context clue:** _____

8. Often people in a clique are <u>gregarious</u>, traveling only with other members of their group as if they were a flock of geese.

   Definition: _____ **Type of context clue:** _____

9. I hope to <u>satiate</u> my hunger by eating that delicious pizza.

   Definition: _____ **Type of context clue:** _____

10. Leading a <u>sedentary</u> lifestyle, or living an inactive life, can lead to serious health problems.

    Definition: _____ **Type of context clue:** _____

from The Perfect Storm

by Sebastian Junger

Summary

Setting: Atlantic Ocean, off the coast of New England, October 1991

The *Satori* is a small sailboat. It is caught in a dangerous storm off the New England coast. Two women and one man are on board. Their life raft is lost. They radio for help. The Coast Guard sends a ship. But it will take the ship many hours to reach the *Satori.* Meanwhile, a small plane finds the *Satori.* The pilot drops life rafts, but they explode when they hit the water. Somehow the *Satori* stays afloat until the Coast Guard ship and a helicopter arrive. Three rescuers in a large raft reach the *Satori,* but the *Satori* accidentally destroys the raft. Now the three rescuers also need to be saved. The helicopter pilot lowers a rescue swimmer and a basket to take the people off the *Satori* one at a time. The first try doesn't work. The *Satori* moves away too fast. Then the pilot tells the *Satori's* crew to put on special suits and jump into the water. One by one, they are helped into the basket by the rescue swimmer and lifted to the helicopter. Then the rescuers are lifted to the helicopter. Everyone heads home.

from The Perfect Storm (page 112)

📖 Active Reading SkillBuilder

Identifying Elements of Storytelling

The Perfect Storm is a nonfiction account of a disaster at sea. When reading the selection, pay attention to the way Junger tells the story. Notice how people in the story are like characters in a work of fiction. Look for important moments of action or conflict, and pay close attention to the setting. Record your observations in the chart below.

Storytelling Elements in *The Perfect Storm*

People in the Story
Captain Leonard worried about losing Satori
Action/Conflict
Setting

from The Perfect Storm (page 112)

Literary Analysis SkillBuilder

Narrative Nonfiction

Nonfiction is writing that deals with real people, places, and events. *The Perfect Storm* is an example of **narrative nonfiction.** It uses elements typically found in fiction, such as plot, character, and setting, to present factual information and bring real events to life. Choose a paragraph from the excerpt with details that seem storylike. Record the details in the box below. Then rewrite the paragraph in a way that is strictly informative, without the intensity or dramatic emphasis of a story.

Details from Paragraph_____ (page_____ column_____)

Rewrite

Follow Up: Did eliminating the elements of fiction affect your enjoyment of the paragraph? Explain.

from **The Perfect Storm (page 112)**

Words to Know SkillBuilder

Words to Know

amalgam	flail	hull	incredulously	maelstrom
despondent	hoist	hypothermic	intermittently	tether

A. Complete each analogy with one of the words from the word list above. In an analogy, the last two words must be related in the same way that the first two are related.

1. JOYOUS : UNHAPPY : : hopeful : _____

2. BRANCH : LIMB : : frame : _____

3. STOP : MOVE : : lower : _____

4. INGREDIENT : RECIPE : : element : _____

5. STILLNESS : CALM : : turbulence : _____

B. For each phrase in the first column, find the phrase in the second column that is closest in meaning. Write the letter of that phrase in the blank.

_____	1. an unusual mixture	A. hoist the Stars and Stripes
_____	2. attach the chain	B. flail furiously
_____	3. thrash about vigorously	C. disturbingly hypothermic
_____	4. a good-looking frame	D. interrupt intermittently
_____	5. examining with disbelief	E. a despondent sailor
_____	6. temperature way too low	F. tie the tether
_____	7. a terrifying situation	G. a handsome hull
_____	8. cut in at intervals	H. an amazing amalgam
_____	9. raise the flag	I. inspecting incredulously
_____	10. a discouraged captain	J. a monstrous maelstrom

C. Write a television news bulletin about the plight of the *Satori.* Use at least **four** Words to Know in your bulletin.

from **The Perfect Storm (page 112)**

....

Selection Quiz

Recall the events in this true story. Then answer the questions in phrases
or sentences.

1. Why are the lives of the *Satori* crew in danger?

   _____

   _____

   _____

2. What help does the pilot of the jet try to provide?

   _____

   _____

   _____

3. Why is time an important factor for everyone involved?

   _____

   _____

   _____

4. What happens when the Avon raft from the *Tamaroa* reaches the *Satori?*

   _____

   _____

   _____

5. What is the outcome of the story?

   _____

   _____

   _____

The Wreck of the Hesperus (page 124)

📖 Active Reading SkillBuilder

Identifying Elements of Storytelling

"The Wreck of the Hesperus" is a narrative poem that tells a story about a disaster at sea. As you read the poem, pay attention to the elements of storytelling. Notice how character is developed. Identify the important moments of action or conflict, and pay close attention to how the setting is described. Use the chart to record these observations.

Storytelling Elements in "The Wreck of the Hesperus"

People in the Story

Action/Conflict

Setting

The Possibility of Evil (page 172)

Literary Analysis SkillBuilder

Characterization

Characterization refers to the way a writer develops characters in a story. There are four basic methods of characterization. A writer may use any or all of the following:

- descriptions of a character's physical appearance
- a character's speech, thoughts, feelings, or actions
- the speech, thoughts, feelings, or actions of other characters
- the narrator's direct comments about a character

Use the chart below to examine the methods of characterization used in "The Possibility of Evil." Record details that help characterize Miss Strangeworth. Tell what each piece of information suggests about her, and identify the method of characterization used by the author.

Miss Strangeworth

What the story says	What it tells me about her	Method of characterization
She walked daintily	Very proper and careful	Physical appearance
Knew everyone in town	Well-known; long-time resident	Direct comment

Follow Up: Write a one- or two-sentence description of Miss Strangeworth based on the details you listed on your chart.

The Possibility of Evil (page 172)

Words to Know SkillBuilder

Words to Know

appropriation	consequently	indulgently	proverbial	reprehensible
banished	degraded	potential	rapt	unchecked

A. Complete each analogy with a word from the word list. In an analogy the last two words must be related in the same way that the first two are related.

1. KIND : MEAN : : blameless : _____

2. LEFT : DEPARTED : : exiled : _____

3. ATTENDED : IGNORED : : restrained : _____

4. DISGUSTED : PLEASED : : bored : _____

5. WELL-LIKED : POPULAR : : well-known : _____

B. For each phrase in the first column, find the phrase in the second column that is closest in meaning. Write the letter of that phrase in the blank.

_____ 1. uncontrolled monkey   A. a reprehensible deed

_____ 2. drive away the beast   B. rapt relatives

_____ 3. therefore no way   C. a proverbial pun

_____ 4. pleasingly tasty   D. proper appropriation

_____ 5. a famous saying   E. indulgently delicious

_____ 6. a blameworthy act   F. consequently can't do it

_____ 7. delighted family   G. a potential problem

_____ 8. really down and out   H. banish the bear

_____ 9. fair financial planning   I. desperate and degraded

_____ 10. a possible dilemma   J. unchecked chimp

C. Suppose that as the director of a production of "The Possibility of Evil," you are to cast the parts. Write an announcement of your choice of an actor to play Miss Strangeworth, explaining why this performer is the best choice. Use at least **four** Words to Know in your announcement.

The Possibility of Evil (page 184)

Grammar SkillBuilder: Proper Nouns

Key Concept: Writers use proper nouns to provide clues about a character or place, to add realism or precision to a story, and to convey tone and attitude.

Proper Nouns

A **proper noun** names a specific person, place, or thing and always begins with a capital letter. Notice the proper nouns in the sentence below. The name of the street, *Pleasant,* suggests something agreeable in contrast to the proper name, *Strangeworth,* which suggests something bizarre. By carefully choosing proper nouns, the author gives the reader a clue that all is not right.

Example: "The perfume of roses meant home, and home meant the <u>Strangeworth</u> house on <u>Pleasant Street</u>."

Activity

Read the following excerpt from Shirley Jackson's story "The Possibility of Evil." Underline all the proper nouns. Which proper nouns provide the reader with clues and information? Explain.

"And good morning to you, too, Mr. Lewis," Miss Strangeworth said at last.

The Lewis family had been in the town almost as long as the Strangeworths;

but the day young Lewis left high school and went to work in the grocery,

Miss Strangeworth had stopped calling him Tommy and started calling him

Mr. Lewis, and he had stopped calling her Addie and started calling her

Miss Strangeworth. They had been in high school together, and had gone

to picnics together, and to high-school dances and basketball games; but

now Mr. Lewis was behind the counter in the grocery, and Miss Strangeworth

was living alone in the Strangeworth house on Pleasant Street.

The Possibility of Evil (page 172)

Selection Quiz

Recall the events in the story. Then answer each question in one or two sentences.

1. Why are so many people in the town upset?

   _____

   _____

   _____

2. How does Miss Strangeworth act toward others when she sees them in person?

   _____

   _____

   _____

3. Why does Miss Strangeworth think she must write letters?

   _____

   _____

   _____

4. How is Miss Strangeworth exposed as the writer of the letters?

   _____

   _____

   _____

5. When Miss Strangeworth receives a letter at the end of the story, how does she react?

   _____

   _____

   _____

The Censors

Luisa Valenzuela

Summary

Setting: Argentina, 1960s–1970s

One day, Juan is happy to get his friend Mariana's new address in Paris. He writes a letter to her without thinking. In Juan's country, mail is censored. Mail is checked carefully in the Censorship Division. Very little is actually sent. Juan and Mariana are now in danger of being kidnapped or worse. He is worried. So he decides to become a censor himself. He hopes to find his letter to make sure that he and Mariana remain safe. Work at the Censorship Division is dangerous. One censor's hand was blown off by a letter bomb. Juan, though, learns his job well. He reports a fellow worker. The worker had tried to organize a strike for higher pay. Juan gets promoted for reporting the worker. Juan now checks letters for poison. He becomes so involved in his work that he forgets his goal. He feels proud of his work. He works to become the perfect censor. Juan's letter to Mariana finally reaches his desk. He censors it like any other. The next day he is executed.

The Censors (page 185)

📖 Active Reading SkillBuilder

Identifying Author's Purpose

A writer can have various purposes for writing. Usually these include one or more of the following:

- to entertain
- to inform or explain
- to express an opinion
- to persuade

As a writer of fiction, Valenzuela surely wanted "The Censors" to entertain. Still, she may have had other purposes. Use the chart below to record the purposes you think Valenzuela had in mind when she wrote the story. Provide evidence from the story to support your ideas.

Purpose	Evidence
Entertain	
Inform or Explain	
Express an Opinion	
Persuade	

The Censors (page 185)

Literary Analysis SkillBuilder

Irony

Irony is the contrast between what is expected and what actually exists or happens.
Situational irony occurs when a character or the reader expects one thing to happen
but something entirely different occurs. **Verbal irony** occurs when one expresses a
meaning by using words that carry the opposite meaning. **Dramatic irony** is the
contrast between what a character knows and what the reader knows. Fill in the blank
in the chart below and then add examples of irony to the chart.

Example of Irony	Type of Irony
Juan is afraid of censorship. BUT: Juan becomes a censor.	Situational irony
Kidnapping is _____. BUT: Kidnapping is called "a noble mission."	

Follow Up: With a partner, discuss which examples of irony on your chart are
playful and poke fun at something and which are serious or tragic.

The Censors (page 185)

....

Words to Know SkillBuilder

Words to Know

conniving   irreproachable   staidness   subtle   subversive

A. Find familiar words in the puzzle below. Circle all the ones you can find that go from left to right or top to bottom in the puzzle. Write them to the right of the puzzle or on a separate sheet of paper.

```
P  R  A  I  S  E  B
R  M  A  P  C  G  A
O  S  V  L  O  U  D
P  L  O  T  L  A  R
E  Y  A  R  D  R  A
R  E  B  E  L  D  G
```

Use five words from the puzzle to fill in the blanks in the following sentences. If you cannot find a word that makes sense and has the correct meaning, look at the puzzle again. Don't use the same word more than once.

1. There would be no reason to _____ an *irreproachable* child.

2. You would expect a _____ response from someone with a reputation for *staidness.*

3. You may do things in a _____ way if you are trying to be *subtle.*

4. A *conniving* plan may be called a _____.

5. One expects *subversive* actions from a _____.

B. Fill in each blank with the correct word from the word list.

1. We tend to expect _____ in older people, even though we allow giddy foolishness in the young.

2. Sensitive people notice even _____ signs of other people's discomfort.

3. No one can plan a surprise party without _____ discussions.

C. In "The Censors," why is it so difficult for a letter to reach its intended recipient? Use at least **three** of the Words to Know in your answer.

The Censors (page 185)

Selection Quiz

Recall the events in this short story. Then answer each question in phrases
or sentences.

1. What happens to the mail in Juan's country?

   _____

   _____

   _____

2. Why does Juan decide to work for the post office?

   _____

   _____

   _____

3. How is Juan able to get promoted?

   _____

   _____

   _____

4. Justifying something he did, Juan tells himself that you don't form a habit by
   doing something once. What does he mean in relation to his own behavior?

   _____

   _____

   _____

5. What happens when Juan's letter to Mariana comes to him?

   _____

   _____

   _____

Analyzing Word Parts—Roots (page 191)
Building Vocabulary SkillBuilder

Identify the root for each word pair and give its meaning. Then use each word
(or a form of the word) in a sentence.

	root	**meaning of root**

1. telegraph/telescope: _____

   Sentences: _____

2. geometry/symmetry: _____

   Sentences: _____

3. biology/zoology: _____

   Sentences: _____

4. suffuse/infuse: _____

   Sentences: _____

5. cardiovascular/cardiology: _____

   Sentences: _____

6. audible/audience: _____

   Sentences: _____

7. contemporary/temporal: _____

   Sentences: _____

8. transitory/transcend: _____

   Sentences: _____

9. interject/reject: _____

   Sentences: _____

10. epidermis/dermatology: _____

   Sentences: _____

Annabel Lee/The Bells (page 198)

📖 Active Reading SkillBuilder

Understanding Poetry

Poe's vocabulary and complex sentence structure can be challenging. When reading the poems, use these suggestions:

• Read each poem aloud to hear the musical quality of the words.

• Pay attention to the punctuation, which can signal breaks or stops, or suggest the mood or emotion behind a phrase.

• Read each poem more than once.

Use the chart below to record any questions you have about the poems. List words, phrases, lines, or passages that you find difficult. Refer to the Guide for Reading annotations for difficult words or phrases, or use a dictionary.

	"Annabel Lee"	"The Bells"
Questions		
Difficult Words or Phrases		

Annabel Lee/The Bells (page 198)

Literary Analysis SkillBuilder

Sound Devices

Poe uses **sound devices** to create a musical effect and emphasize ideas. **Rhyme** is the occurrence of a similar or identical sound at the ends of two or more words. **Alliteration** is the repetition of consonant sounds at the beginnings of words. **Assonance** is the repetition of vowel sounds within nonrhyming words. On the chart below, list examples of sound devices that you find in Poe's poems. Then explain the effects these sound devices create.

	Rhyme	Alliteration	Assonance
"Annabel Lee"			
"The Bells"			

Effects:

The Cask of Amontillado

Edgar Allan Poe

Summary

Setting: Italy or France, early spring, late 1700s to early 1800s

Montresor has been insulted by Fortunato. Montresor decides to get revenge. One night during a festival, Montresor comes across Fortunato. Fortunato is drunk and off guard. Montresor knows that Fortunato is proud of his fine taste in wines. He tells Fortunato that he has bought some Amontillado wine. He tells Fortunato that he is not sure if the Amontillado is the real thing. Fortunato wants to taste the wine to be sure. Montresor takes Fortunato deep into his wine cellars. They come to a small, dark room. Montresor says that the Amontillado is in the room. Fortunato steps into the room. Quickly, Montresor chains him to the wall. Fortunato does not realize what is happening until it is too late. Little by little, Montresor walls up the entrance to the room with stone. At first, Fortunato thinks it is a joke. Then he cries out for mercy. Montresor ignores him. He leaves Fortunato to die.

The Cask of Amontillado (page 207)

Active Reading SkillBuilder

Making Inferences

Making an **inference** is figuring something out on the basis of evidence. Readers usually infer by combining clues in the text with what they already know from their own experiences or other reading. Think about the actions, thoughts, and feelings of the narrator in "The Cask of Amontillado." Look for insights into his motivation. Record any observations that provide clues about the narrator's state of mind.

What the Narrator Says	What I Can Infer
The thousand injuries of Fortunato I had borne as I best could; but when he ventured upon insult, I vowed revenge.	The narrator feels that he has been injured by Fortunato's insults.

Name _____ Date _____

The Cask of Amontillado (page 207)

Literary Analysis SkillBuilder

Mood

The overall feeling or atmosphere that a writer creates for the reader is called **mood.**
Descriptive words, the setting, and figurative language, as well as the sound and
rhythm of the language the writer uses, contribute to the mood of a work. On the
chart below, list examples of passages that help create the mood of the story. Identify
the kind of mood that is created and explain how the mood is developed.

Passage	Mood that Is Created	How Mood Is Developed
"We are below the river's bed. The drops of moisture trickle among the bones."	gloomy, creepy, chilly, dark and damp	descriptive words, setting

Follow Up: How do you react to the overall mood of this story? Discuss your
thoughts and feelings with a group of classmates.

The Cask of Amontillado (page 207)

Words to Know SkillBuilder

Words to Know

accost	fetter	impunity	repose	termination
destined	implore	preclude	subside	virtuoso

A. Each of the following sentences suggests a word in the word list. The word itself is hidden in the sentence. Underline the hidden word and then write it on the line. An example, using another word from the story, has been done for you.

Example: Using a tool like a shovel, I dug the first <u>row. E</u>llen came along behind me, putting the seeds in place.

_____ *trowel*

The guy in the monster outfit stopped me with a paw and snarled right in my face. I said, "Back off, Mac. Costume party or no costume party, I'm not putting up with this."

_____
(1)

We'll scoop up the money and take off in the blimp. Unity is the key here. If we stick together, we'll get away with it for sure!

_____
(2)

Oh, no! An all-you-can-eat buffet! Terrible things will happen to my diet if you don't handcuff me and chain me to my chair!

_____
(3)

It has a certain poetic sound, but don't say, "He was bound from birth to be the baddest." In educated speech, that would be "Fated to be the worst," even if doesn't sound as good.

_____
(4)

In the book's drawings, cats of all kinds are posed on chairs and sofas, sleeping soundly and dreaming of mice.

_____
(5)

B. For each phrase in the first column, find the phrase in the second column that is closest in meaning. Write the letter of that phrase in the blank.

_____ 1. to ask again   A. virtuoso, better than so-so

_____ 2. to snugly rest   B. to implore some more

_____ 3. to decline everywhere   C. to fetter better

_____ 4. the end of a holiday   D. to cozily repose

_____ 5. highly skilled, above average   E. to subside worldwide

_____ 6. to more effectively restrain   F. to preclude a brooding mood

_____ 7. to prevent a sad frame of mind   G. an opportunity for impunity

_____ 8. the chance to avoid consequences   H. the termination of a vacation

C. Describe Montresor's crime in a statement that could be used to support a charge of murder against him. Use at least **five** of the Words to Know.

The Cask of the Amontillado (page 219)

Grammar SkillBuilder: Compound Verbs

Key Concept: Writers use compound verbs to combine several short sentences into longer, more interesting sentences.

Compound Verbs

A **compound verb** in a sentence consists of two or more verbs that have the same subject and are connected by a conjunction. Some conjunctions that may connect verbs are *and, but,* and *or.* If the compound verb has three or more verbs, a comma follows each verb or verb phrase except the last.

"We **came** at length to the foot of the descent **and stood** together on the damp ground of the catacombs of the Montresors." (*We* is the subject of both verbs.)

Activity

Use compound verbs to combine each set of sentences into a single sentence.
Example: Montresor selects a bottle of Medoc. He opens it. He urges Fortunato to drink.
Rewritten: Montresor <u>selects</u> a bottle of Medoc, <u>opens</u> it, and <u>urges</u> Fortunato to drink.

1. Montresor has been insulted by Fortunato. He vows revenge.

2. Montresor, a connoisseur of Italian wines, buys quantities of it whenever possible. He stores them in his wine cellar.

3. Meeting Fortunato at the carnival, Montresor greets him warmly. He tells him about the Amontillado. He asks him to come and taste it.

4. Montresor hands Fortunato a lighted torch. He cautions Fortunato to watch his step.

5. Fortunato raises the Medoc to his lips. He tastes it. He nods his approval.

6. As they advance, the niter increases. It hangs like moss upon the vaults.

7. The interior recess was constructed for no special use. It was simply formed by the space between two large supports of the roof.

8. Fortunato steps unsteadily forward. He reaches the end of the interior recess. He stands there bewildered.

9. Montresor uncovers a quantity of stone and mortar. He begins to wall up the entrance to the recess.

10. Before completing the wall, Montresor pauses. He holds the torch over it. He allows some light to fall upon the chained Fortunato.

The Cask of Amontillado (page 207)

Selection Quiz

Recall the events in this classic horror story. Then answer each question in phrases or sentences.

1. What is Montresor's attitude toward revenge, or punishment?

   _____

   _____

   _____

2. How does Montresor get Fortunato to do the opposite of what he is asking of him?

   _____

   _____

   _____

3. Why do you think Montresor gives Fortunato bottles to drink on their way to taste the Amontillado?

   _____

   _____

   _____

4. Where does Montresor take Fortunato to get his revenge?

   _____

   _____

   _____

5. What is Montresor's revenge?

   _____

   _____

   _____

Opinion Statement

Prewriting

Before writing your opinion statement, use the chart below to sketch out different sides of the issue. Then state your opinion and analyze your stand on the issue. List any facts you already know that support your opinion. Also list additional facts that you need to find.

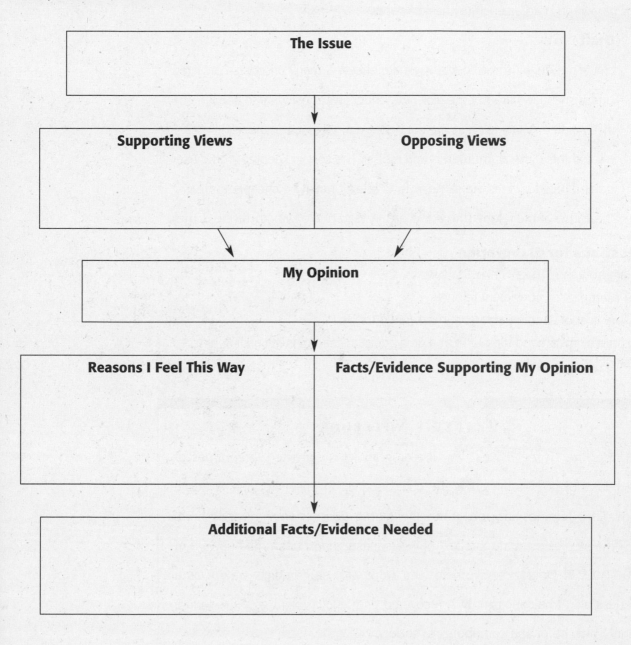

The Issue

Supporting Views | **Opposing Views**

My Opinion

Reasons I Feel This Way | **Facts/Evidence Supporting My Opinion**

Additional Facts/Evidence Needed

Opinion Statement

Drafting and Elaboration

The paragraph below is from a draft of a student's opinion statement about the "Three Strikes" law. It needs more details and statistics to make the student's opinion more convincing. Revise the paragraph by following the Suggestions for Elaboration and using the information in the Reader's Notebook. Copy your revised paragraph onto a separate sheet of paper.

Draft

Even though "Three Strikes" laws are effective, many prisoners convicted under such laws are not the violent offenders we most want to see incarcerated. Many felonies are not necessarily violent, but these inmates are treated the same as murderers and rapists. The cost of keeping a drug user behind bars for life is the same as for a killer. It might be cheaper to treat the cause of the felony (the addiction) instead of the symptom (the crime).

Suggestions for Elaboration
- Explain how the "Three Strikes" law works.
- Give examples of nonviolent felonies.
- Cite the cost of keeping a person incarcerated for life.
- Explain why it's a good idea to treat a drug addict instead of incarcerating him or her.

READER'S NOTEBOOK

■ Under the "Three Strikes" law, if a drug addict is convicted three times of the felony of possessing drugs, he could end up in prison for life. ■ Some nonviolent felonies include grand theft, drug possession, embezzlement.
■ Some studies estimate the cost of incarcerating a prisoner for life upward of $500,000. ■ Doctors and others who work with drug addicts view it as a sickness akin to alcoholism. ■ A recovered drug addict might go on to lead a life in which he or she contributes to society.

Opinion Statement

Peer Response Guide

Have you adequately expressed your views in your opinion statement? It can be hard to know. To find out how well you've made your point, ask a friend or classmate to respond to the following questions.

1. What is my opinion about this issue? Does my position come across clearly?

   Response:

   Suggestions for Revision:

2. What are my strongest supporting points?

   Response:

   Suggestions for Revision:

3. What are my weakest supporting points? How can I improve them?

   Response:

   Suggestions for Revision:

Peer Response Guide continued

4. Is any information unnecessary?

Response:

Suggestions for Revision:

5. What more would you like to know about the issue or my opinion?

Response:

Suggestions for Revision:

6. Did my opinion statement make you think about the issue in a different way? Why or why not?

Response:

Suggestions for Revision:

Opinion Statement

Revising, Editing, and Proofreading

Revising

TARGET SKILL ▶ Supporting Statements with Facts and Examples

As you revise your opinion statement, ask yourself the following questions.

- Have I used facts and examples to support my opinion?
- Have I cited information when quoting sources?
- Is my tone appropriate for my target audience?
- Have I given my sentences enough variety in terms of length and structure?

Editing and Proofreading

TARGET SKILL ▶ Subject-Verb Agreement

Refer to the bulleted list below to help you edit this paragraph from a draft of one student's opinion statement about the "Three Strikes" law. Use proofreading marks to correct errors in grammar, usage, mechanics, and spelling. Then copy your corrected draft onto a separate sheet of paper.

- Make sure each verb agrees with its subject in number.
- Vary sentence beginnings.
- Rewrite run-on sentences and avoid short, choppy sentences.
- Use word choice and language appropriate for audience.

Draft

I think that the "Three Strikes" law is not a good law. I think deep down we all believes this. I believe a nonviolent offender should not be treated the same as a murderer and then be given a life sentence like a murderer who is incarcerated for violence and the nonviolent offender are just someone who skimmed a few bucks. Its pretty rotten. Think about it. Some people are in prison for life. And all they did is committ three nonviolent offences.

Applying

Now edit and proofread your own opinion statement. Refer to the bulleted list above.

Opinion Statement

Strong Student Model

High School Teams Should Be Coed

In the years since the groundbreaking feminism of the 1960s, women have gained equality with men in many areas of life in the United States. We have women judges and women governors, near-equal pay between the sexes, and such an acceptance of women's equality among young people like myself that the chauvinism of my parents' generation seems quite offensive. The one place where men and women are still treated unequally is in the arena of high school athletics. As a woman and an athlete, I believe this last frontier should be broken through. High school sports teams should be made up of players of both sexes.

Throughout their school careers, girls and boys compete in everything equally. They take the same tests, attend the same classes, vie for the same academic awards and scholarships. Why not compete in sports? An athlete is driven to be the best—not just in terms of his or her gender but in terms of all athletes. That drive to be the best is the nature of the athletic desire, and because of it we have championship games and school rivalries and all of those things that allow an athlete to declare "I am the best." However, a woman athlete will never know if she can beat everyone; she'll know only that she can beat her own gender.

Could there actually be a reason for this separation of male and female athletes? Opponents to coed teams point to old-fashioned ideas about what boys can do and what girls cannot. Yet women have shown they are athletically equal to men in many sports. Both Cynthia Cooper and Sheryl Swoopes of the WNBA Houston Comets are as fast and talented as just about any male player in the NBA. Florence Griffith-Joiner and Wilma Rudolph are considered to be among the all-time greatest runners of *either* sex. Martina Navratilova changed the way an entire generation plays tennis, male or female. These athletes are as good as anyone, regardless of their gender.

Still, opponents to coed athletics say that girls are just too frail to compete against boys. But where is that "frailty" a problem? Most sports are not violent contact sports. Baseball, basketball, soccer, and track are more about skills

1. Establishes issue clearly in introduction.

2. States opinion clearly at close of introductory paragraph.

3. Uses comparison and contrast to begin argument.

4. Rhetorical question helps direct argument and introduces opposing view.

5. Specific examples challenge opposing view and support writer's opinion.

6. Challenges opposing argument with well-chosen examples.

Strong Student Model continued

than they are about physical contact. Even a sport as violent as football has sometimes admitted women. We have all heard of the girl high school quarterback (a television movie was even made of her story), as well as girl kickers. These girls were picked for the team because they were the best at what they did. If there had been better players available, the girls would not have been given the positions. Team selection should always be that way.

No one has a problem with girls and boys competing with and against each other in physical education classes. Throughout middle school, boys and girls form up teams during gym class, and there are no cries from concerned parents about "frail" girls. Even intramural softball teams have girl players. My parents play on the same softball team on weekends, and my mom usually hits more home runs than my dad does.

7. Makes comparison to similar situation to bolster argument.

8. Investigates another opposing argument to determine its validity.

Boys who hear about possible coed teams claim the girls will weaken the team. A chain is only as strong as its weakest link, they say, and they point to the girls who are terrible at sports. This is not fair. Nonathletic girls won't go out for teams with boys on them; they don't go out for teams with girls on them, so why would they change their behavior? This is true of boys, too. The nonathletic boys don't go out for football unless they really want to play. If they want to play, they *can* try out. Girls should have the same opportunity.

9. Facts about women's physical capabilities support opinion.

10. Restates opinion strongly in the conclusion.

Saying a team is only as strong as its weakest player and then pointing to a girl is offensive. Women have higher endurance, are lighter, and can maneuver on their feet more easily than men. Many play as well as or better than the average male athlete. So what valid reason is there to continue sexism in sports? None that makes sense. Isn't it time to be a good sport so that all athletes can compete fairly?

Opinion Statement

Average Student Model

Make High School Teams Coed

These days women have gained equality with men in most areas of life. Think about it! We have women judges and women governors, near-equal pay between the sexes, and women commanding big box office at the movies. Men can no longer make sexist remarks without everybody finding them offensive. But there is still one place where men and women are not equal. That's right: high school athletics. I am a woman and an athlete, and I think this last frontier needs to be torn down. High school sports teams should be made up of players of both sexes.

All through school, girls and boys compete in everything equally. We take the same tests, attend the same classes, stand in the same cafeteria lines. Why not compete in sports? What does it mean to be an athlete? It means to give your all to be the best. But if you're a girl, and you're the best in your division, you still don't know whether you're better than the boys. Just because boys and girls have separate locker rooms, it doesn't mean that they can't be on the same team. The way things are—it's just not fair play.

Some opponents to coed teams spout a lot of old-fashioned nonsense about how boys can do this and how girls cannot. It's just not true. Women have shown they are athletically equal to men in many sports. There are players in the WNBA who could easily take on NBA players if given the chance. And some of the best runners of all time have been women. And you can't think of tennis without thinking of the women who have won Wimbledon over the years. These women are as good as anyone, male or female.

Some people say that girls are just too frail to compete against boys. That doesn't really apply to anything but football. Most sports are not violent contact sports. Baseball, basketball, soccer, and track are more about skills than they are about how frail or burly a player is. Even football sometimes has women players. Some years ago there was a girl high school quarterback (I saw a TV movie about her), and girls have played as kickers. These girls made the team because they were the best. If there had been better players, the girls would not have been given the positions.

1. *Establishes issue clearly—if a bit informally—in introduction.*

2. *States opinion at the close of introductory paragraph.*

3. *Begins argument with comparison and contrast.*

4. *Informal tone is wrong for audience.*

5. *Examples support argument but should include specific names and/or statistics.*

6. *Begins sentences with* and *or* but *too often throughout essay.*

7. *Specific examples challenge opposing view and supports opinion.*

Average Student Model continued

Why does team make-up change in high school? No one has a problem with girls and boys competing with and against each other in physical education classes. In middle school boys and girls form up teams during gym class, and no one complains about "frail" girls. Even intramural softball teams have girl players. My mom and dad play on the same softball team on weekends, and she usually hits more home runs than he does. But it is different in high school. I ask you, why?

8. Example points out flaw in opposing argument.

Some vocal boys complain that girls will weaken the team. They point to the girls who are terrible at sports and say, "How can we win with *her* on the team?" This is totally unfair. Wimpy girls won't go out for teams with boys on them; they don't go out for teams with girls on them, so why would they suddenly act differently? This is true of wimpy boys, too. The wimpy boys don't go out for football unless they really want to play. If they want to play, they can try out. Girls should have the same opportunity.

9. Argument is good, but tone is far too informal.

When you stop and think about it, all of this talk about how weak girls are is offensive. Basically, they are saying that girls are losers. But if they are so certain girls are losers, then they should let the girls have a chance and play with and against them. What are they afraid of? Are they afraid that girls might win? Are they afraid that girls might become the most valuable players on their teams? Isn't it time to make high school teams coed so that we can find out?

10. Informal language is inappropriate for audience.

11. Series of questions is a strong way to end statement, but informal tone weakens argument.

Opinion Statement

Weak Student Model

Make Sports Coed!

1. The writer establishes issue somewhat informally.

These days women are equal with men in most areas of life. We have women judges and women governors. Women get almost equal pay for the same jobs men do. Like men, women also get to star in movies. Men don't make as many sexist remarks as they use to do. But there is still one issue which men and women are not equal— high school athletics. I am a woman and an athlete. I think having different teams for boys and girls is bogus.

2. States opinion, but tone makes opinion sound like a complaint.

3. Uses comparison and contrast, but informal tone is not persuasive.

Why should sports be different than everything else at school? We have the same tests, go to the same classes, and eat in the same cafeteria. Why not have the same sports? Shouldnt girls be allowed to be their best? Isnt that what it is all about? If we are going to have to sit in classes with boys, we should be able to throw footballs with them and tag them out at first. Because boys and girls have separate locker rooms, doesnt mean that they cant play sports together. Its not fair.

4. Contractions are written incorrectly throughout essay.

5. Reasoning makes opposition sound silly and can easily be countered.

Some people say girls are too "frail" to go against boys. They make you think that girls go out on the field in dresses, and worry about every smudge on their uniform. Or that if they get pushed down that the girls would break down and cry or something. Get real. Girls are tough when they compete. Anyone who has watched a WNBA game can see that these women are dead serious about their sport. The only thing that is girlish about them is the thing that they cant get away from: theyre women.

6. The writer expresses good ideas, but they are vague.

Another Option:
• *Use well-chosen examples to support opinion.*

7. Needs to supply more facts to strengthen support.

How many sports are very physical, anyway? Not baseball or track. And basketball is only when the players push each other around. Football is physical and sometimes even violent. But there have been girl quarterbacks—at least on TV movies. So why not in real life? Are girls bones harder to break? Sure, boys are bigger and stockier. But women are smaller and faster. These different physical attributes balance out, I think.

Those who are against coed teams like to repeat a lot of old-fashioned nonsense about how boys can do this and how girls can't. Its just not true. Women have proved they are the equal to any man in sports. There have been women basketball players, women tennis players, women runners, and more. They have all done as well as a man

8. Specific names or statistics would strengthen support.

Weak Student Model continued

might. These women are as good as anyone, male or female.

Why does team make-up change in high school? No one raises a stink when girls and boys compete with each other in physical education classes. In middle school boys and girls form up teams during gym class, and no one complains about "frail" girls. Even intramural softball teams have girl players. My mom and dad play on the same softball team on weekends. And my mom usually hits more home runs than he does. But it is different in high school. I ask you, why?

9. Argument is good, but tone is still too informal.

10. Informal language is inappropriate for audience.

Some boys complain that girls will make their teams weak. They point to the wimpy girls and say, "How can we win with *her* on the team?" This is so unfair. Wimpy girls wont go out for teams with boys on them; they dont go out for teams with girls on them, so why would they suddenly act different? This is true of wimpy boys, too. The wimpy boys dont go out for football unless they really want to play. If they want to play, they can try out. And if they are good enough they make the grade. Girls should have the same opportunity.

When you stop and think, all of this talk about how weak girls are is silly. Basically, they are saying that girls are losers. But I believe they should let the girls have a chance and play with and against them.

11. Conclusion is incomplete.

Other Options:
• Summarize supporting arguments.
• Clearly restate opinion.

Opinion Statement

Rubrics for Evaluation

Ideas and Content	Weak	Average	Strong
1. Clearly states the issue and opinion of it in the introduction			
2. Supports opinion with convincing examples, facts, and statistics			
3. Uses language and details appropriate for the audience			
4. Addresses opposing viewpoints where appropriate			

Structure and Form			
5. Uses clear transitions to signal new points			
6. Sums up opinion in the conclusion			
7. Subjects and verbs agree throughout			

Grammar, Usage, and Mechanics			
8. Contains no more than three minor errors in grammar and usage			
9. Contains no more than three minor errors in spelling, capitalization, and punctuation			

Writing Progress to Date (Writing Portfolio)

The strongest aspect of this writing is _____
_____

The final version shows improvement over the rough draft in this way: _____
_____

A specific improvement over past assignments in your portfolio is _____
_____

A skill to work on in future assignments is _____

Additional comments: _____
_____

Reviewing Literary Concepts (page 227)

Reflect and Assess

OPTION 1 **Analyzing conflict**

Selection	Type of Conflict	Description of Conflict	Effect on Main Character

Answer Key
Unit One

The Necklace
Active Reading SkillBuilder, page 5
(Responses will vary. Possible responses are provided that continue the series on the worksheet.)
- Madame Loisel buys a new dress and borrows a friend's diamond necklace to wear to the party.
- On the way home from the party, Madame Loisel loses the necklace.
- The Loisels search for the missing necklace in vain.
- The Loisels borrow money and use an inheritance to buy another diamond necklace to replace the lost one.
- Madame Loisel returns the necklace to Madame Forestier.
- The Loisels live in poverty for ten years until they repay all of their debts.

The Necklace
Literary Analysis SkillBuilder, page 6
(Responses will vary. Possible responses are provided.)
Rising Action: 1. The Loisels are invited to a party. 2. Madame Loisel borrows a diamond necklace to wear to the party. 3. She loses the necklace on the way home. 4. The Loisels search for the necklace to no avail.
Climax: The Loisels borrow money and use an inheritance to buy a diamond necklace to replace the one lost after the party. (Note: Some students may defend the idea that the climax comes at the very end of the story.)
Falling Action: 1. Madame Loisel returns the necklace to Madame Forestier. 2. Because they are in debt, the Loisels are forced to live like paupers. 3. After ten years, the Loisels finally repay all of their debts. 4. Madame Loisel discovers that Madame Forestier's lost necklace was an imitation worth a fraction of the diamond necklace that replaced it.
Follow Up: Responses depend on events students list.

The Necklace
Words to Know SkillBuilder, page 7
A. 1. adulation
2. pauper
3. prospects
4. exorbitant
5. aghast
6. ruinous
7. privation
8. vexation
9. askew
10. gamut

B. Students' columns will vary. Accept responses that accurately use at least five Words to Know.

Grammar SkillBuilder
Abstract and Concrete Nouns, page 8
(Answers will vary.)
1. Mathilde Loisel lacked the distinguished <u>family</u> and the <u>dowry</u> that would permit her to marry a man of rank.
2. Though she had a pretty <u>face</u> and a pleasant <u>voice</u> and manner, she finally married a minor clerk.
3. Her apartment looks <u>shabby</u> and <u>drab</u> to her.
4. Her reaction to the invitation is one of bleak <u>distress</u>.
5. She says she has no suitable <u>dress</u> or <u>jewels</u>.
6. Her husband responds with <u>consideration</u> and <u>generosity</u>.
7. She examines the <u>bracelets</u> and <u>necklaces</u> in her friend's jewel <u>box</u>.
8. She dances every <u>waltz</u> and enjoys admiring <u>glances</u>.
9. She reacts to the loss of the necklace with helpless <u>grief</u> and <u>despair</u>.
10. Mme. Loisel learns to wash <u>dishes</u>, scrub <u>clothes</u>, and bargain with the <u>grocer</u>.

The Necklace
Selection Quiz, page 9
1. Madame Loisel is unhappy because she was born into a middle-class family and had no dowry and no chance to meet a wealthy man to marry. She feels she should be leading a life of more luxury.
2. Madame Loisel and her husband spend their savings to buy her a fancy dress. She borrows a necklace from a well-to-do friend.
3. Madame Loisel loses the necklace she borrowed.
4. Madame Loisel is too embarrassed and ashamed to tell her friend that she has lost the necklace. She thinks it is worth a lot of money.
5. The Loisels have worked for ten years to repay the huge sum of money that they borrowed to buy the replacement necklace. Her friend tells her that the original was worth only a relatively small amount of money because it was not made of real diamonds.

The Most Dangerous Game
Active Reading SkillBuilder, page 11
(Responses will vary. Possible responses are provided.)
Prediction: I predict that Zaroff will hunt Rainsford.
Reasons: Zaroff claims he hunts an animal that can reason, and he is becoming bored with his most recent quarry—shipwrecked sailors.
Prediction: I predict that Rainsford will successfully elude Zaroff.

Reasons: Zaroff believes Rainsford is a worthy opponent, and Rainsford is an accomplished hunter himself.

Prediction: I predict that Rainsford will kill Zaroff.

Reasons: At the end of the story, Zaroff is too cocky; he says that only one person will sleep in his bed.

The Most Dangerous Game
Literary Analysis SkillBuilder, page 12
(Responses will vary. Possible responses are provided.)

Internal Conflict
Zaroff: He has always considered hunting his life, but has grown bored with it and must find ways to make it exciting again.

Rainsford: He feels fear and panic after leaving Zaroff's chateau, but forces himself to keep his nerve and use his wits and his skill as a hunter to devise a logical plan for his escape.

External Conflict
Person vs. person: Rainsford fights for his life against the hunter Zaroff.

Person vs. nature: Rainsford struggles to survive at sea after he falls overboard.

Person vs. obstacle: Zaroff manages to avoid the Malay man-catcher and the Burmese tiger pit, two of the traps created by Rainsford.

Follow Up: Students will most likely say that the external conflict between Rainsford and Zaroff added the most excitement to the story. Some students may say that Rainsford's internal conflict revealed important character traits that helped them understand his motivations and actions. Students may say that Connell added the other conflicts in the story to provide interest and suspense and to help move the plot along.

The Most Dangerous Game
Words to Know SkillBuilder, page 13
A. 1. deplorable
2. affable
3. disarming
4. amenity
5. uncanny
6. tangible
7. solicitously
8. imperative
B. 1. C
2. F
3. E
4. B
5. D
6. G
7. A

C. Students' character sketches will vary. Accept responses that accurately use at least five Words to Know.

Grammar SkillBuilder
Choosing Precise Verbs, page 14
(Answers will vary.)
1. drowses
2. springs
3. leaps
4. plunges
5. drags
6. crawl
7. stretches
8. freezes
9. bursts
10. stumble

The Most Dangerous Game
Selection Quiz, page 15
1. Rainsford thinks hunting is the best sport in the world.
2. Rainsford is on his yacht at night when he hears shots from a nearby island. He stands on the rail to see better and accidentally falls overboard. He swims through rough seas to reach the island. The next day, he sees a chateau, knocks on the door, and meets Zaroff.
3. Zaroff proposes that Rainsford join him in hunting humans because hunting dangerous animals has become boring.
4. Rainsford uses hunting tricks—such as digging a pit, setting up a booby trap, and causing Zaroff's dogs to lose his scent—to help him on the island.
5. Rainsford has jumped off a cliff to escape Zaroff and his dogs. Zaroff thinks Rainsford is dead, but Rainsford swims to safety and surprises Zaroff in his house.

Where Have You Gone, Charming Billy?
Active Reading SkillBuilder, page 17
(Responses will vary. Possible responses are provided.)
Statement in Story: "In the morning, when they reached the sea, he would begin to make friends with some of the other soldiers."
Common Sense: Because this is Paul's first day in the war, he has not yet had time to become acquainted with the soldiers in his platoon.
Inference: Paul feels lonely and isolated.
Statement in Story: "He would tell his mother how it smelled . . . But he would not tell how frightened he had been."

Common Sense: People do not want to admit their feelings when they are ashamed or embarrassed.

Inference: Paul is ashamed of being afraid.

Statement in Story: "The giggles were caught in his throat, drowning him in his own laughter: scared to death like Billy Boy."

Common Sense: People who feel nervous or frightened sometimes laugh inappropriately to cover their true feelings.

Inference: Paul is terrified.

Where Have You Gone, Charming Billy?

Literary Analysis SkillBuilder, page 18

(Responses will vary. Possible responses are provided.)

Toby ("Buffalo"): Toby's reassurance that it has been a bad day calms Paul; his conversation about Billy Boy makes Paul break out in nervous giggles.

Billy Boy Watkins: Paul's witnessing Billy Boy's death from a heart attack triggers his fears about fighting in the war and makes him pretend that he is a boy again.

The Unseen Enemy: Paul walks carefully on the path because he fears being killed or maimed by hidden land mines and booby traps.

Paul's Father: Paul's thoughts of his father buoy his spirits, boost his courage, and lessen his feelings of isolation and alienation, but also increase his shame of being afraid.

Follow Up: Students may say that Paul's conflict, which is primarily internal, is his fear of fighting. They may say that Billy Boy Watkins and the unseen enemy contribute to Paul's conflict but that Toby and his father help him resolve it.

Where Have You Gone, Charming Billy?

Words to Know SkillBuilder, page 19

A.
1. comfort
2. gracefully
3. perform
4. unfocused
5. outlined
6. informally
7. clear

B.
1. transparent
2. silhouetted
3. diffuse
4. conical
5. primitive
6. inertia
7. elegantly
8. execute

C. Students' letters will vary. Accept responses that accurately use at least three Words to Know.

Grammar SkillBuilder

Adverbs, page 20

(Answers will vary.)
1. extremely—anxious, adjective
2. always—appear, verb
3. slowly—moved, verb
4. awkwardly—crawled, verb
5. horribly—afraid, adjective
6. very—heavy, adjective
7. steadily—marched, verb; almost—silently, adverb
8. cautiously—followed, verb; desperately—tried, verb
9. patiently—waited, verb
10. finally—reached, verb; much—better, adverb

Where Have You Gone, Charming Billy?

Selection Quiz, page 21
1. Berlin is in Vietnam because he is a soldier (private first class) and there is a war there.
2. Berlin is afraid because it is his first day of war, and the conditions are extremely dangerous. He is also afraid of dying in the same way Billy Boy did—that is, from fear itself.
3. He pretends he is not in a war but on a camping trip with his father. He also counts his steps and sings songs in his head, but his strategies don't work because his mind keeps going back to Billy Boy's accident and death.
4. Billy Boy Watkins is injured by a land mine and loses his foot. He is so afraid of dying that he has a heart attack. Berlin cannot stop thinking about the circumstances of Billy Boy's death and how his body fell from the helicopter.
5. It is important that Toby smother Berlin's giggling because it is hysterical and uncontrollable and the noise of it may reveal their position to the enemy.

Marigolds

Active Reading SkillBuilder, page 23

(Responses will vary. Possible responses are provided.)

Text Information: The children hate Miss Lottie's marigolds.

Prior Knowledge: People usually hate things that are ugly or unpleasant.

Conclusion: The blooming flowers, which represent the beauty that the children do *not* have in their lives, serve as a painful reminder of their poverty and grim surroundings.

Text Information: Miss Lottie never planted marigolds again.

Prior Knowledge: People always find time and energy to pursue activities they enjoy.

Conclusion: When the narrator destroyed the marigolds, she also destroyed Miss Lottie's enthusiasm for gardening.

Marigolds

Literary Analysis SkillBuilder, page 24
(Responses will vary. Possible responses are provided.)
Passage 1: "I remember only the dry September of the dirt roads and grassless yards . . . Miss Lottie's marigolds" (page 76).
Feelings the Setting Expresses: deprivation, sterility, barrenness, hope
Passage 2: "Miss Lottie's house was the most ramshackle. . . . a monument to decay" (page 78).
Feelings the Setting Expresses: instability, insecurity, impermanence, depression
Follow Up: Students' poems will vary but should incorporate specific descriptive phrases that they underlined in the story passages on their charts.

Marigolds

Words to Know SkillBuilder, page 25
A. 1. bravado
   2. impotent
   3. impoverished
   4. degradation
   5. perverse
   6. compassion
   7. stoicism
   8. futile
   9. squalor
   10. poignantly
"Marigolds" takes place during the Depression.

B. Students' apologies will vary. Accept responses that accurately use at least five Words to Know.

Grammar SkillBuilder

Compound Adjectives, page 26
(Answers will vary.)
 1. *hot, dusty* summer
 2. children, *bored* and *restless,*
 3. *bright, amazing* marigolds
 4. is old, *white-haired, and shaky*
 5. *wild, unprovoked* attack
 6. *strong, laughing* father
 7. *confused* and *fearful* mood
 8. is sorry, *ashamed,* and *miserable*
 9. *senseless, violent* act
 10. emotional, *long-ago* time

Marigolds

Selection Quiz, page 27
 1. Lizbeth remembers the shanty-town's dust and the sunny yellow color of Miss Lottie's marigolds.
 2. She remembers feeling as if she were leaving childhood. She recalls the "chaotic emotions of adolescence." She and her brother played and laughed together and continued doing childish mischief, but she was aware that she was changing into an adult.
 3. Lizbeth says Miss Lottie was old and bent, though she had once been tall and powerful. She never left her yard and did not like intruders. Her house was the most rundown of all the ramshackle houses. It was gray and rotting, barely standing, with no shutters or steps. Her yard had no grass or weeds, but it had mounds of marigolds next to her house.
 4. They throw pebbles at her flowers, cutting off the blooms. They dance in a circle around her, screaming, "old lady witch."
 5. Lizbeth, restless and unable to sleep, runs back to Miss Lottie's house with her brother Joey and destroys the marigolds.

Two Kinds

Active Reading SkillBuilder, page 29
(Responses will vary. Possible responses are provided.)
List of Criteria: Is the complaint realistic? Is it believable? Is it based on fact?
Mother's Complaint: The mother complains that her daughter doesn't try hard enough.
Justified: yes
Daughter's Complaint: The daughter complains that her mother doesn't like her the way she is.
Justified: yes
Mother's Complaint: The mother complains that her daughter doesn't do the chores her parents ask her to do because she hears nothing but music.
Justified: no
Daughter's Complaint: The daughter complains that she is bored with her mother's tests.
Justified: yes

Two Kinds

Literary Analysis SkillBuilder, page 30
(Responses will vary. Sample responses are provided.)
What Daughter Learns: The daughter learns that she cannot always please her mother. She was right to believe that she should be herself because her mother's expectations were not realistic.
What Mother Learns: The mother learns that she can't change her daughter to be what she wants her to be. Her expectations were too high. Her daughter failed and will fail, which is reasonable.
Theme: You have to live your own life and be yourself; you can't always live to fulfill others' expectations.

Two Kinds

Words to Know SkillBuilder, page 31
A. 1. fiasco
   2. reproach

3. prodigy
4. devastate
5. discordant

B. 1. D
    2. A
    3. E
    4. B
    5. C

C. Students' contrasts will vary. Accept responses that accurately use at least five Words to Know.

Grammar SkillBuilder
Verb Phrases, page 32
(Answers may vary.)
1. did write; has written
2. was listed; had been listed
3. was made; has been made
4. are woven
5. is narrated
6. could be
7. had given; was giving
8. was focused; was focusing
9. might have become
10. could have been

Two Kinds
Selection Quiz, page 33
1. Jing-mei is excited, imagining herself as a child movie star or a ballerina. She thinks she will become perfect at something, and then her parents will adore her.
2. Jing-mei hates to keep failing and seeing the disappointment in her mother's face.
3. She learns a lot about music and the piano, but she also learns that she can trick Mr. Chong and get away with a lot of mistakes.
4. Jing-mei has not practiced, and she plays very poorly. She shames herself and her family.
5. After the talent show, Jing-mei and her mother have an argument. Jing-mei says she wishes she were dead, like her mother's twin baby girls in China. The argument damages their relationship for many years.

Building Vocabulary SkillBuilder
Understanding Context Clues, page 34
1. **definition:** loud argument or disagreement
   type of clue: example
2. **definition:** to persuade with flattery or deception
   type of clue: restatement
3. **definition:** difficult to work with
   type of clue: comparison
4. **definition:** agree
   type of clue: contrast

5. **definition:** to overlook or disregard poor or offensive behavior
   type of clue: example
6. **definition:** forgetting all details or clueless
   type of clue: comparison or example
7. **definition:** to submit to someone else's wishes or opinions
   type of clue: example
8. **definition:** tending to move in a group as if in a herd, flock, or pack
   type of clue: restatement
9. **definition:** to satisfy a desire
   type of clue: example
10. **definition:** sitting and having little activity
   type of clue: definition

from The Perfect Storm
Active Reading SkillBuilder, page 36
(Responses will vary. Possible responses are provided.)
People in the Story: Crew of the *Satori*—Bylander, Stimpson, Leonard—face life-or-death situation; members of the Coast Guard risk their lives in failed rescue effort; Dave Moore successfully rescues both *Satori* and Avon crews.
Action/Conflict: humanity struggling against nature; the race against time; the dramatic steps in the perilous rescue; the Coast Guard's failed attempts; Moore's heroic rescues
Setting: fierce winds and huge waves in the stormy Atlantic Ocean; cold, difficult to see, but the "water is lukewarm"; "seas are so big they give him [Moore] the impression he's swimming uphill and downhill rather than over individual waves"

from The Perfect Storm
Literary Analysis SkillBuilder, page 37
(Students' choices of paragraphs will vary. A sample response for paragraph 2, page 114, column 1, is provided.)
Details from Paragraph: the sound of an airplane fading in and out through the roar of the storm; a Falcon jet shrieking overhead; Bylander frantically radioing for help; Stimpson relieved to be in touch with life outside again
Rewrite: Students' rewritten paragraphs will vary.
Follow Up: Students' discussions should reveal an awareness of how adding the elements of fiction to nonfiction can add drama and heighten the reader's interest.

from The Perfect Storm
Words to Know SkillBuilder, page 38
A. 1. despondent
    2. hull

3. hoist
4. amalgam
5. maelstrom

B. 1. H
  2. F
  3. B
  4. G
  5. I
  6. C
  7. J
  8. D
  9. A
  10. E

C. Students' bulletins will vary. Accept responses that accurately use at least four Words to Know.

from The Perfect Storm
Selection Quiz, page 39

1. The lives of the *Satori* crew are in danger because their boat is disabled in the midst of a terrible storm. They have no life raft, and the quickest rescue is twelve hours away.
2. The pilot drops two life rafts tied to a long nylon rope. The drop is aimed perfectly but the rafts explode when they hit the water.
3. It is getting late in the day, and a rescue would be impossible after dark. The storm is not only dangerous for the stranded crew but for everyone involved in the rescue attempts.
4. The Avon raft is punctured by the *Satori* as the sailboat rocks wildly in the storm. The three rescuers on the Avon boat are now also stranded.
5. Dave Moore, a rescue swimmer, helps each member of the crew into a hoist basket so that one by one they can be hoisted into the helicopter. Then the Coast Guard rescuers are hoisted to safety. Everyone is rescued.

The Wreck of the Hesperus
Active Reading SkillBuilder, page 40
(Responses will vary. Possible responses are provided.)
People in the Story: skipper, skipper's daughter, old Sailor, crew, fisherman
Action/Conflict: Despite a warning from the old Sailor, the skipper decides to sail the schooner through a treacherous winter storm. The skipper, his crew, and his daughter all die either from the extreme cold or from the ship being wrecked on the reef of Norman's Woe.
Setting: dangerous ocean storm in winter; "The snow fell hissing in the brine/And the billows frothed like yeast"; "gleaming snow"; "whistling sleet and snow"

The Wreck of the Hesperus
Literary Analysis SkillBuilder, page 41
(Responses will vary. Possible responses are provided.)
Overall Feeling Poem Conveys: danger, doom, disaster
Lines That Reflect Overall Feeling: lines 15–16, 25–28, 41–48, 61–68, 77–88
Follow Up: Students' discussions will vary. In their discussions, students should suggest either general kinds of music or specific compositions that fit the poem's subject matter and overall feeling.

O What Is That Sound
Active Reading SkillBuilder, page 55
(Responses will vary. Possible responses are provided.)
First Speaker
Identity: perhaps a woman who is in love with the second speaker
First Reaction to Sound: curiosity
Later Reaction to Sound: fear, dread
Second Speaker
Identity: perhaps a political rebel
First Reaction to Sound: explains matter-of-factly that the sound is the drumming of soldiers
Later Reaction to Sound: leaves abruptly to either join or to flee from the soldiers

O What Is That Sound
Literary Analysis SkillBuilder, page 56
(Responses will vary. Possible responses are provided.)
Questions for First Speaker: 1. Do you suspect that the soldiers are coming toward your house? 2. Do you feel as if no one is telling the truth about this serious situation?
Questions for Second Speaker: 1. What war or battle is going on? 2. Are the soldiers coming for you to join them? 3. Why are you so calm?

Incident in a Rose Garden
Active Reading SkillBuilder, page 57
(Responses will vary. Possible responses are provided.)
Setting: blooms "strewed the earth" in the rose garden
Characters: gardener—"old man, out of breath"; "Fear had given him legs"; Death—"thin as a scythe"; dressed in black coat, gloves, and hat; has big mouth with white teeth
Events: Death picks the master's blooming roses one by one and smells them; Death grins evilly at the master; Death shakes the master's hand with his "little cage of bone."

Incident in a Rose Garden

Literary Analysis SkillBuilder, page 58
(Responses will vary. Possible responses are provided.)
Description: Death—human figure
Figure of Speech: Personification
Effect Created: creates interest
Description: Death—Spanish waiter
Figure of Speech: Simile
Effect Created: creates a vivid visual image in the reader's mind, adds humor
Description: Death's eyes—lanterns
Figure of Speech: Metaphor
Effect Created: adds dimension, creates a precise mental picture
Description: Death's hand—cage of bone
Figure of Speech: Metaphor
Effect Created: appeals to the senses of sight and touch

The Gift of the Magi

Active Reading SkillBuilder, page 60
(Predictions will vary. Possible responses are provided.)
1. Della does not have enough money to buy a Christmas present because she counts out $1.87 three times and then howls.
2. Della will sell her hair to Madame Sofronie because she turns pale and cries when she looks at her hair in the glass.
3. Della will buy Jim a nice present because she receives $20 for selling her hair and immediately goes shopping.

The accuracy of students' predictions will vary.

The Gift of the Magi

Literary Analysis SkillBuilder, page 61
(Responses will vary. Possible responses are provided.)
What Della plans: to surprise her husband, Jim, with a Christmas present of a fob chain for his pocket watch
What actually happens: She finds out that Jim has sold his precious pocket watch to buy her a Christmas present.
What Jim plans: to surprise his wife, Della, with a set of expensive hair combs that he buys with the money he gets from selling his watch
What actually happens: He finds out that Della has cut her hair and sold it in order to get the money for his Christmas present.

The Gift of the Magi

Words to Know SkillBuilder, page 62
A. 1. cascade
2. coveted
3. predominating

4. subside
5. instigate
Della receives combs.
B. 1. predominating
2. coveted
3. assertion
4. agile
5. subside
6. prudence
7. inconsequential
8. cascade
9. instigate
10. chronicle
C. Students' entries will vary. Accept responses that accurately use at least three Words to Know.

Grammar SkillBuilder

Pronouns, page 63
(Answers will vary.)
1. Della wants to buy a Christmas present for Jim, but she has only $1.87.
2. Della visits a woman who buys hair, and the woman pays her $20.00 for her long hair.
3. The gift that Della selects for Jim is a chain for his pocket watch, which is the thing he values most.
4. When Jim sees Della with short hair, he doesn't show anger but stares at her peculiarly.
5. Jim has given Della the set of combs that she has long wanted for the cascading hair of which she is so proud.
6. O. Henry implies that the two "foolish children" are really wise because they give each other gifts of love.
7. O. Henry, whose real name was William Sydney Porter, wrote about 300 stories; like one of his own stories, his life was full of twists and turns.
8. The young Porter was raised by a grandmother and aunt who took him in after the death of his mother.
9. Years after working as a bank clerk, Porter was accused of embezzlement, and he spent three years in jail for the crime.
10. During his time in jail, Porter perfected the short story style that made him famous.

The Gift of the Magi

Selection Quiz, page 64
1. It is Christmas Eve and Della is unhappy because she has only been able to save $1.87 to buy a present for her husband, Jim.
2. Della decides to cut her long hair and sell it. She does so and receives $20. Happily she goes shopping for a present for Jim.

3. Jim is stunned because he loved Della's beautiful hair and he never expected her to have it cut.

4. His present to her is a set of tortoise-shell combs to be worn in long hair. She had admired them.

5. Della is at first very emotional—full of joy, then bursting into tears. She then becomes philosophical, saying that her hair grows quickly. Jim is calmer. He just smiles and says they should put their presents away for the time being.

The Sniper
Active Reading SkillBuilder, page 66
(Responses will vary. Possible responses are provided.)
Setting: "Dublin lay enveloped in darkness"; "machine guns and rifles broke the silence of the night, spasmodically, like dogs barking on lone farms"
Characters: sniper's eyes "had the cold gleam of the fanatic"; the enemy sniper "was now standing before a row of chimney pots, looking across, with his head clearly silhouetted against the western sky"
Action: "The distance was about fifty yards—a hard shot in the dim light. . . . He took a steady aim." "The sniper darted across the street. A machine gun tore up the ground around him, but he escaped."

The Sniper
Literary Analysis SkillBuilder, page 67
Students' ranking of suspenseful events will vary but will most likely indicate a steady increase in level of suspense from the first event to the last event listed on the graph.

The Sniper
Words to Know SkillBuilder, page 68
A. 1. C
2. F
3. D
4. G
5. A
6. H
7. I
8. B
9. J
10. E
B. Students' editorials will vary. Accept responses that accurately use at least four Words to Know.

Grammar SkillBuilder
Adverb Placement, page 69
(Answers may vary.)
1. Listening <u>carefully</u> for suspicious sounds, the sniper considered lighting his cigarette.
2. He <u>boldly</u> decided to risk it and lit the cigarette.
3. <u>Then</u> a shot rang out, and he dropped his rifle.

4. He had been shot in his arm, but <u>surprisingly</u> he felt no pain.
5. <u>Immediately</u> he dropped to the roof and crawled behind a chimney.
6. While he hid behind the chimney, his enemy watched <u>silently</u> from the opposite roof.
7. The sniper placed his cap over the muzzle of his rifle, <u>cleverly</u> fooling his enemy.
8. After he was wounded, the sniper lifted his revolver and <u>awkwardly</u> fired.
9. The gunfire was over, and <u>soon</u> three people were dead.
10. <u>Always</u>, in a civil war, there is a danger of killing a brother or friend.

The Sniper
Selection Quiz, page 70
1. The Republicans are fighting the Free Staters. The sniper is on the Republican side.
2. The sniper lights a match and the flare is seen by a gunman on another roof.
3. By shooting the man and woman, the sniper again exposes himself to the gunman. He is shot and badly wounded in the arm.
4. The gunman is fooled by a trick the sniper plays. The sniper places his hat on his rifle muzzle and extends it over the parapet, draws the gunman's fire, and then lets the hat and the rifle fall to the street below. The gunman, thinking the sniper is dead, stands up. The sniper then shoots the gunman with a revolver.
5. The gunman is the sniper's own brother.

The Possibility of Evil
Active Reading SkillBuilder, page 72
Students' word webs will vary. Details may include the following: walks daintily; careful; tends roses; is 71 years old; lives alone; tidy; keeps an immaculate house; writes anonymous letters.

The Possibility of Evil
Literary Analysis SkillBuilder, page 73
(Responses will vary. Possible responses are provided.)
What the story says: Miss Strangeworth thinks the town belongs to her.
What it tells me about her: She cares deeply about the town and what happens to it.
Method of characterization: the character's thoughts
What the story says: Miss Strangeworth doesn't sign her letters and mails them secretly at night.
What it tells me about her: She doesn't want anyone to know who is writing the letters.

Method of characterization: the character's actions
What the story says: Children in town treat her respectfully.
What it tells me about her: She is one of the town's most important citizens.
Method of characterization: the other characters' actions
Follow Up: Students may say that the elderly Miss Strangeworth is a proper, moral woman. As a prominent citizen, she feels it is her duty to rid her town of evil, but misguidedly sends the townspeople cruel, anonymous letters that point out their wrongdoing.

The Possibility of Evil
Words to Know SkillBuilder, page 74
A. 1. reprehensible
   2. banished
   3. unchecked
   4. rapt
   5. proverbial
B. 1. J
   2. H
   3. F
   4. E
   5. C
   6. A
   7. B
   8. I
   9. D
   10. G
C. Students' announcements will vary. Accept responses that accurately use at least four Words to Know.

Grammar SkillBuilder
Proper Nouns, page 75
(Answers may vary.)
   "And good morning to you, too, <u>Mr. Lewis</u>," <u>Miss Strangeworth</u> said at last. The <u>Lewis</u> family had been in the town almost as long as the <u>Strangeworths</u>; but the day young <u>Lewis</u> left high school and went to work in the grocery, <u>Miss Strangeworth</u> had stopped calling him <u>Tommy</u> and started calling him <u>Mr. Lewis</u>, and he had stopped calling her <u>Addie</u> and started calling her <u>Miss Strangeworth</u>. They had been in high school together, and had gone to picnics together, and to high-school dances and basketball games; but now <u>Mr. Lewis</u> was behind the counter in the grocery, and <u>Miss Strangeworth</u> was living alone in the <u>Strangeworth</u> house on <u>Pleasant Street</u>."

The proper nouns: Miss Strangeworth, Tommy, Mr. Lewis, Addie, and Pleasant Street provide the reader with clues about the odd nature of Miss Strangeworth. Although Miss Strangeworth and Mr. Lewis had been friends in high school, Miss Strangeworth stopped addressing her friend by his first name once out of school. Her attempt to be proper and formal is carried to an extreme. And like the name of her street, she appears pleasant, but she is really a strange person as emphasized by her name.

The Possibility of Evil
Selection Quiz, page 76
   1. The townspeople are upset because they have been getting nasty letters from an anonymous letter writer.
   2. She is polite and friendly to everyone.
   3. Miss Strangeworth thinks it is her duty to write the letters "as long as evil existed unchecked in the world." She is the last Strangeworth and it is up to her to keep her town from falling into evil.
   4. When Dave Harris sees Miss Strangeworth drop a letter at the post office, he picks it up, sees that it is addressed to Don Crane, and decides to deliver it in person on his way home.
   5. The letter is like one of her own—mean-spirited—and she sees it as more evidence that there is evil in the world.

The Censors
Active Reading SkillBuilder, page 78
(Responses will vary. Possible responses are provided.)
Purpose: to entertain
Evidence: Valenzuela describes censorship in a playfully ironic way.
Purpose: to inform or explain
Evidence: Valenzuela explains how personal letters are censored in a dictatorship.
Purpose: to express an opinion
Evidence: Valenzuela does not believe in dictatorships because she mocks the way the fictional government attempts to control its citizens.
Purpose: to persuade
Evidence: The underlying theme of the story is that censorship is wrong and should be resisted.

The Censors
Literary Analysis SkillBuilder, page 79
(Responses will vary. Possible responses are provided.)
Example of Irony: Kidnapping is a crime. BUT: Kidnapping is called "a noble mission."
Type of Irony: Verbal

Example of Irony: Censorship limits the rights of citizens. BUT: Censoring letters is called a "patriotic task."
Type of Irony: Verbal
Example of Irony: Juan does an excellent job as a censor. BUT: He is executed because he censors his own letter to Mariana rather than intercepting it as he originally planned.
Type of Irony: Situational
Follow Up: Students may comment that the examples of verbal irony on their charts are more playful, as well as any irony that pokes fun at Juan's dilemma. Examples of irony, particularly dramatic irony, that address kidnapping, persecution, or execution are serious and tragic.

The Censors
Words to Know SkillBuilder, page 80
A. **Words in the Puzzle:** *(across)* praise, raise, map loud, plot, lot, yard, rebel *(down)* prop, proper, rope, roper, sly, lye, scold, cold, old, guard, bad, drag, rag
   1. scold
   2. proper
   3. sly
   4. plot
   5. rebel
B. 1. staidness
   2. subtle
   3. conniving
C. Students' answers will vary. Accept responses that accurately use at least three Words to Know.

The Censors
Selection Quiz, page 81
   1. The mail is censored so that the censors will know what people are thinking or planning.
   2. Juan wants a job as a censor so that he can intercept the letter he wrote to Mariana and protect himself and her from danger.
   3. Juan is able to get promoted by reporting a fellow worker for trying to organize a strike.
   4. Juan believes that he has not made a habit of reporting his coworkers because he did it only once.
   5. Juan reads his own letter to Mariana as if it were any other, and he censors it.

Building Vocabulary SkillBuilder
Analyzing Word Parts—Roots, page 82
(Students' sentences may vary. Samples are given.)
   1. **root:** *tele*
      root's meaning: far, distant
      Sentences: Before there were telephones, people used telegraphs to send information quickly. The astronomy class uses a high-powered telescope to view the constellations.

   2. **root:** *metry*
      root's meaning: process of measuring
      Sentences: Part of geometry is studying different shapes and their properties. One such property is symmetry.
   3. **root:** *ology*
      root's meaning: the science or study of
      Sentences: Biology is the study of living things, including animals. Zoology is only the study of animals, and does not include all of biology.
   4. **root:** *fus*
      root's meaning: to pour
      Sentences: The iced tea has been suffused with lemon. Her speech infused the group with new enthusiasm.
   5. **root:** *cardio*
      root's meaning: heart
      Sentences: In the field of cardiology, or study of the heart, studies suggest that cardiovascular exercise is best for preventing heart disease.
   6. **root:** *audio*
      root's meaning: hearing; sound
      Sentences: The audience could hear the actors because microphones and speakers made them audible.
   7. **root:** *tempor*
      root's meaning: time
      Sentences: That painting is contemporary to the era in which the house was built. We are temporal beings, with our lives being limited to about 80 years.
   8. **root:** *trans*
      root's meaning: across
      Sentences: That was a transitory romance, only lasting a week. On the other hand, their feelings still transcend what would be usual for "just friends."
   9. **root:** *ject*
      root's meaning: throw, hurl
      Sentence: Joshua chose to interject comments while his opponent spoke, even though he knew the idea would be rejected.
   10. **root:** *derma*
       root's meaning: skin
       Sentence: The dermatologist can help you with any skin problems you have. The epidermis is the thin outer layer of your skin.

Annabel Lee/The Bells
Active Reading SkillBuilder, page 83
Students' questions and challenges will vary. They should use the suggestions listed for understanding poetry and the Guide for Reading to help clarify the meanings of difficult words, phrases, lines, or passages that they encounter in the poems.

Annabel Lee/The Bells
Literary Analysis SkillBuilder, page 84
(Responses will vary. Possible responses are provided.)
Annabel Lee
Rhyme: sea, Lee, me; beams, dreams
Alliteration: half, happy, Heaven; demons, down
Assonance: out, cloud; life, bride
The Bells
Rhyme: notes, floats, gloats; fire, higher, desire
Alliteration: merriment, melody; tale, terror, tells
Assonance: molten, golden, notes; silence, night
Effects: Students may say that Poe's use of sound devices in "Annabel Lee" emphasizes the musical qualities of the language, reinforces the speaker's sense of loss, and heightens the mood of sadness. They may say that his use of sound devices in "The Bells" helps re-create the actual sounds of the bells and establish the different moods of the situations for which the bells ring.

The Cask of Amontillado
Active Reading SkillBuilder, page 86
(Responses will vary. Possible responses are provided.)
What the Narrator Says: "These orders were sufficient, I well knew, to insure their immediate disappearance, one and all, as soon as my back was turned."
What I Can Infer: The narrator wants to make sure that his servants leave the palace.
What the Narrator Says: "You are rich, respected, admired, beloved; you are happy, as once I was."
What I Can Infer: The narrator is deeply unhappy.
What the Narrator Says: "My heart grew sick—on account of the dampness of the catacombs."
What I Can Infer: The narrator does not feel guilt for what he has done to Fortunato, or he is trying to deny it.

The Cask of Amontillado
Literary Analysis SkillBuilder, page 87
(Responses will vary. Possible responses are provided.)
Passage: "I had scarcely laid the first tier . . . feeble rays upon the figure within." (pages 212–214)
Mood That Is Created: despair, fear
How Mood Is Developed: by the use of descriptive words, by the sound and rhythm of the language
Passage: "A succession of loud and shrill screams . . . the clamorer grew still." (page 214)
Mood That Is Created: terror, horror
How Mood Is Developed: by the use of descriptive words, setting, figurative language
Follow Up: Students' reactions to the overall mood of the story will vary.

The Cask of Amontillado
Words to Know SkillBuilder, page 88
A. 1. Mac. Costume; accost
2. blimp. Unity; impunity
3. buffet! Terrible; fetter
4. baddest." In educated; destined
5. are posed; repose
B. 1. B
2. D
3. E
4. H
5. A
6. C
7. F
8. G
C. Students' statements will vary. Accept responses that accurately use at least five Words to Know.

Grammar SkillBuilder
Compound Verbs, page 89
(Answers may vary.)
1. Montresor has been insulted by Fortunato and vows revenge.
2. Montresor, a connoisseur of Italian wines, buys quantities of it whenever possible and stores them in his wine cellar.
3. Meeting Fortunato at the carnival, Montresor greets him warmly, tells him about the Amontillado, and asks him to come and taste it.
4. Montresor hands Fortunato a lighted torch but cautions him to watch his step.
5. Fortunato raises the Medoc to his lips, tastes it, and nods his approval.
6. As they advance, the niter increases and hangs like moss upon the vaults.
7. The interior recess was constructed for no special use but was simply formed by the space between two large supports of the roof.
8. Fortunato steps unsteadily forward, reaches the end of the interior recess, and stands there bewildered.
9. Montresor uncovers a quantity of stone and mortar and begins to wall up the entrance to the recess.
10. Before completing the wall, Montresor pauses, holds the torch over it, and allows some light to fall upon the chained Fortunato.

The Cask of Amontillado

Selection Quiz, page 90

1. He believes that revenge is punishment without punishment in return.
2. Montresor tells Fortunato that he will ask Luchesi's opinion of his new wine. Fortunato insists that he is a better judge of wine.
3. Montresor gives Fortunato bottles of wine to drink to make him think he is on his way to the wine cellar and to make him even more intoxicated than he is.
4. He takes him into the catacombs of the Montresor family.
5. Montresor chains Fortunato to the wall of a recess in the crypt and then walls up the entrance, leaving him to die.